The Life of Animals
with Backbones

FOUNDATIONS OF SCIENCE LIBRARY

The Natural World
(4 volumes)

The Majesty of the Heavens
(Foundations of Astronomy)

The Round World
(Foundations of Geology and Geomorphology)

The Skies and the Seas
(Foundations of Meteorology, Oceanography & Cartography)

The Ages of the Earth
(Foundations of Palaeogeography and Palaeontology)

The Biological Sciences
(6 volumes)

The Life of Animals without Backbones
(Foundations of Invertebrate Zoology)

The Life of Animals with Backbones
(Foundations of Vertebrate Zoology)

The World of Plants
(Foundations of Botany)

Breeding and Growing
(Foundations of Genetics, Anthropology and Agriculture)

Patterns of Living
(Foundations of Ecology)

Human Kind
(Foundations of Human Biology)

The Physical Sciences
(9 volumes)

The Restlessness of Matter
(Foundations of Aerodynamics, Hydrodynamics and Thermodynamics)

The Science of Movement
(Foundations of Mechanics and Sound)

Lightning in Harness
(Foundations of Electricity)

The Silent Energy
(Foundations of Electrical Technology)

The Cathode Ray Revolution
(Foundations of Electronics)

The Rays of Light
(Foundations of Optics)

The Unseen Spectrum
(Foundations of Electromagnetic Radiation)

The Cosmic Power
(Foundations of Nuclear Physics)

The Discipline of Numbers
(Foundations of Mathematics)

The Chemical Sciences
(4 volumes)

The Fundamental Materials
(Foundations of Basic Chemistry)

The Elements and their Order
(Foundations of Inorganic Chemistry)

The Giant Molecules
(Foundations of Organic Chemistry)

The Chemist at Work
(Foundations of Analysis and Laboratory Techniques)

Technology
(5 volumes)

The Metallic Skills
(Foundations of Metallurgy)

Industrial Processing
(Foundations of Industrial and Chemical Technology)

Engineering Technology
(Foundations of Applied Engineering)

Automobile Engineering
(Foundations of Car Mechanics)

The Inventive Genius
(Foundations of Scientific Inventions)

History and Reference
(3 volumes)

The Beginnings of Science
(Foundations of Scientific History)

Frontiers of Science
(Foundations of Research Methods)

A Dictionary of Scientific Terms
(The Foundations of Science Reference Book)

CHIEF EDITORS
Leslie Basford, B.Sc.   Philip Kogan, M.Sc.

ASSISTANT EDITORS
Michael Dempsey, B.A., Michael Gabb, B.Sc., Clare Dover, B.Sc.
Cyril Parsons, B.Sc., Joan Pick, B.Sc., Michael Chinery, B.A.
David Larkin, B.Sc., Paul Drury Byrne, B.Sc.

CONSULTANT EDITORIAL BOARD
Sir Lawrence Bragg, M.C., O.B.E., F.R.S., M.A., Nobel Laureate
Sir James Chadwick, F.R.S., Ph.D., M.Sc., Nobel Laureate
Norman Fisher, M.A.
Sir Harry Melville, K.C.B., F.R.S., Ph.D., D.Sc.
Professor J. Z. Young, F.R.S., M.A.

The Life of Animals with Backbones

Foundations of Vertebrate Zoology

MICHAEL GABB B.Sc. MICHAEL CHINERY B.A.

FOUNDATIONS OF SCIENCE LIBRARY
THE BIOLOGICAL SCIENCES

DISTRIBUTED IN THE U.S.A. BY
Ginn and Company : *BOSTON*
PUBLISHED BY
Sampson Low, Marston and Co : *LONDON*

This new presentation assembles
freshly edited material from
'Understanding Science' on one
subject into a single volume.

Copyright © 1966 Sampson Low, Marston & Co. Ltd.

SBN 356 00023 0

Library of Congress Catalog Card
Number: 66–17996

Catalog No.: L–20735

Made and printed in Great Britain by
Purnell & Sons Ltd., Paulton
(Somerset) and London

VERTEBRATE ZOOLOGY

Contents

The Classification of Animals

PHYLUM PROTOZOA (Single-celled animals)

Amoeba (Protozoa)

Foraminifera (Protozoa)

PHYLUM PORIFERA (Sponges)

Glass sponge (Porifera)

Crumb o' Bread sponge (Porifera)

PHYLUM CNIDARIA (Jellyfishes, corals, hydroids, sea anemones, sea firs, sea pens)

PHYLUM CTENOPHORA (Sea gooseberries, comb jellies)

Jellyfish (Cnidaria)

Sea gooseberry (Ctenophora)

PHYLUM PLATYHELMINTHES (Flatworms, tapeworms, flukes)

Flatworm (Platyhelminthes)

PHYLUM ANNELIDA (Earthworms, bristle worms, leeches)

Leech (Annelida)

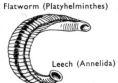

Tube-worm (Annelida)

PHYLUM CHAETOGNATHA (Arrow worms)

Sea mouse (Annelida)

PHYLUM NEMERTEA (Proboscis worms)

Arrow worm (Chaetognatha)

PHYLUM NEMATODA (Roundworms)

Hookworm (Nematoda)

Proboscis worm (Nemertea)

PHYLUM BRYOZOA (Moss animals)

Moss animal (Bryozoa)

PHYLUM NEMATOMORPHA (Hairworms)

PHYLUM ROTIFERA (Wheel animalcules)

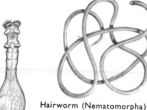
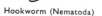

Hairworm (Nematomorpha)

PHYLUM BRACHIOPODA (Lamp shells)

Callidina (Rotifera)

Lamp shell (Brachiopoda)

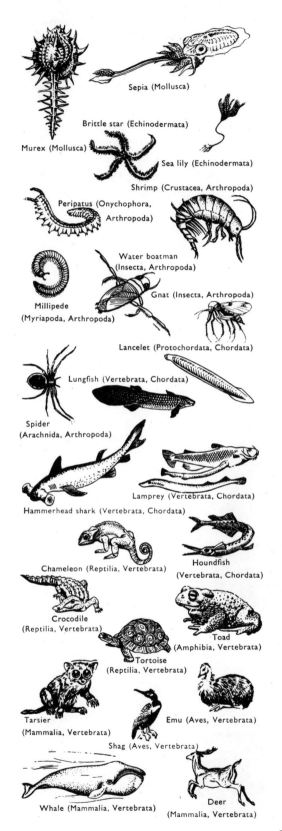

Sepia (Mollusca)

Brittle star (Echinodermata)

Murex (Mollusca)

Sea lily (Echinodermata)

Shrimp (Crustacea, Arthropoda)

Peripatus (Onychophora, Arthropoda)

Water boatman (Insecta, Arthropoda)

Gnat (Insecta, Arthropoda)

Millipede (Myriapoda, Arthropoda)

Lancelet (Protochordata, Chordata)

Lungfish (Vertebrata, Chordata)

Spider (Arachnida, Arthropoda)

Lamprey (Vertebrata, Chordata)

Hammerhead shark (Vertebrata, Chordata)

Chameleon (Reptilia, Vertebrata)

Houndfish (Vertebrata, Chordata)

Crocodile (Reptilia, Vertebrata)

Toad (Amphibia, Vertebrata)

Tortoise (Reptilia, Vertebrata)

Tarsier (Mammalia, Vertebrata)

Emu (Aves, Vertebrata)

Shag (Aves, Vertebrata)

Whale (Mammalia, Vertebrata)

Deer (Mammalia, Vertebrata)

PHYLUM MOLLUSCA (Gastropods, bivalves, octopuses, squids, amphineurans)

PHYLUM ECHINODERMATA (Sea urchins, starfishes, sea cucumbers, sea lilies, brittle stars)

PHYLUM ARTHROPODA (Onychophora, insects, crustaceans, spiders and scorpions, millipedes and centipedes)

PHYLUM CHORDATA (Protochordates, vertebrates)

Protochordata (Lancelets, sea squirts, acorn worms)

Vertebrata (Lampreys, cartilage fishes, bony fishes, lungfishes, amphibians, reptiles, birds, mammals)

5

THE animal kingdom is divided into many groups, the largest of which are called phyla (singular phylum). The members of each phylum have certain features in common which distinguish them from members of other phyla. The largest phylum, in terms of numbers of species, is the Arthropoda, but perhaps the most varied phylum is the Chordata. It is a large phylum containing animals ranging from fishes, through snakes and tortoises, to birds, bats and elephants. Despite these seemingly vast differences, the chordates have many features in common, as will be explained in this book.

The phylum Chordata is divided into a number of smaller groups. The protochordates are small animals – sea squirts, acorn worms, and lancelets – showing some connections with other phyla. All other chordates have backbones or vertebral columns and are called *vertebrates*. The vertebrates include fishes, amphibians, reptiles, birds and mammals. This book deals only with the vertebrates.

A RED SQUIRREL
(Mammalia, Vertebrata)

The Vertebrate Plan

CHAPTER ONE

The Structure of Chordate Animals

Animals in the group that includes the sea squirts, acorn worms, lancelets, hagfishes and lampreys, fishes, amphibians, reptiles, birds and mammals are called *chordates* (the group name is *Chordata*). At some stage in their life chordates have *gill slits*, a supporting rod of elastic material, the *notochord*, and a *hollow dorsal nerve cord*.

THE FEATURES OF A TYPICAL CHORDATE

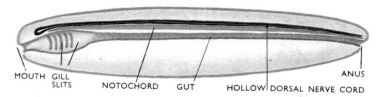

MOUTH GILL SLITS NOTOCHORD GUT HOLLOW DORSAL NERVE CORD ANUS

The larva of a tunicate (sea squirt) shows clearly the basic chordate features, far better than the adult does. It has a hollow dorsal nervous system, the tail is supported by a notochord, and though the gut is not well developed (the larva does not feed) it usually has a pair of gill slits.

The adult tunicate has no notochord, and the central nervous system is a solid nerve mass or ganglion, but the pharynx has gill slits whose cilia beat to draw a water current carrying food and oxygen. There is no coelom but a body cavity of another kind is present.

LARVAL TUNICATE

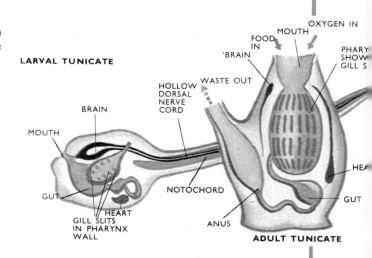

BRAIN
MOUTH
HOLLOW DORSAL NERVE CORD
GUT
GILL SLITS IN PHARYNX WALL
HEART
NOTOCHORD
ANUS

OXYGEN IN
MOUTH
FOOD IN
'BRAIN
PHARY SHOW GILL S
WASTE OUT
HEA
GUT

ADULT TUNICATE

The lancelet (*Amphioxus*) displays the features of a typical chordate. The body is fish-shaped and flattened from side to side. The muscles consist of a series of blocks, the fibres of which work to bend the body from side to side. The gut is a long tube with a mouth and anus and the wall of the pharynx is perforated by gill slits; the gills are ciliated. The cilia beat to draw a water current containing food into tne pharynx. There is a coelom (body cavity) around the gut. The notochord is an elastic rod (the length of the body) beneath the hollow dorsal nerve cord. It stops the body from shortening when it bends during movement. The skin consists of only one layer.

AMPHIOXUS
(cutaway)

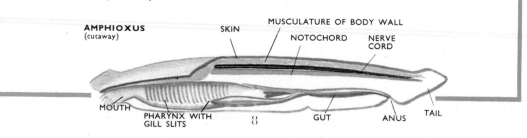

SKIN
MUSCULATURE OF BODY WALL
NOTOCHORD
NERVE CORD
MOUTH
PHARYNX WITH GILL SLITS
GUT
ANUS
TAIL

All other chordates have a skull (*cranium*) and a backbone (*vertebral column*), though the latter is not always well developed – they are called *vertebrates*. The front end of the nervous system is enlarged to form a brain. Associated with this are the special sense organs – the eyes, nose and ears. The pharynx is small compared with that of the invertebrate chordates and the gills are used in respiration and *not* for food collecting. The vertebrate blood system has a heart with at least three chambers (*Amphioxus* has no heart) and there is an internal skeleton of bone and/or cartilage. The skin is many-layered.

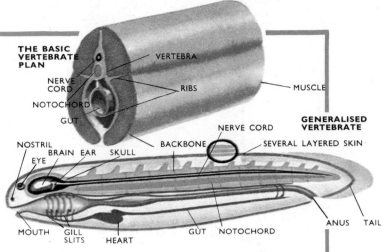

THE BASIC VERTEBRATE PLAN

VERTEBRA
NERVE CORD
RIBS
MUSCLE
NOTOCHORD
GUT

GENERALISED VERTEBRATE

NOSTRIL
EYE
BRAIN EAR SKULL
BACKBONE
NERVE CORD
SEVERAL LAYERED SKIN
ANUS TAIL
MOUTH
GILL SLITS
HEART
GUT NOTOCHORD

The simplest vertebrates (lampreys, hagfishes, etc.) have no jaws. The mouth is surrounded by a large, round sucker. The tail has a fin which extends forwards halfway along the back and the muscle blocks are W-shaped. The skeleton is made up of the notochord and cartilage.

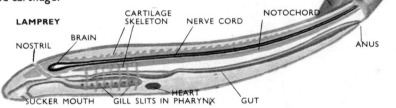

LAMPREY

NOSTRIL
BRAIN
CARTILAGE SKELETON
NERVE CORD
NOTOCHORD
FIN MUSCLE
ANUS
SUCKER MOUTH
GILL SLITS IN PHARYNX
HEART
GUT

The sharks, rays and skates (cartilaginous fishes) have an internal skeleton of cartilage – bone is entirely absent. They are the simplest of the living vertebrates with jaws. The 'skull' is better developed than in the jawless vertebrates. In all except the king herring the gill slits are visible and not covered by a gill flap or operculum as in bony fishes. The gills are respiratory. The skin is covered with horny teeth-like scales and on the jaws these are modified to form teeth. The dorsal lobe of the tail is larger than the ventral lobe. Besides the dorsal fins (typically two in number) there are two pairs of paired fins. Each paired fin has a supporting structure at the base – *pectoral* (shoulder) girdle and *pelvic* (hip) girdle. The notochord is reduced and largely replaced by vertebrae – short ribs are present in the front region. Movement is produced mainly by the serial contraction of the fibres of successive muscle blocks – arranged essentially as in simpler chordates. The gut is more elaborate and divided into more obvious regions.

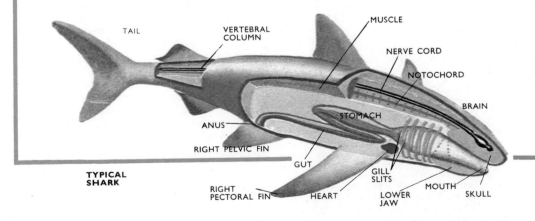

TAIL
VERTEBRAL COLUMN
MUSCLE
NERVE CORD
NOTOCHORD
BRAIN
ANUS
STOMACH
RIGHT PELVIC FIN
GUT
GILL SLITS
MOUTH
SKULL
RIGHT PECTORAL FIN
HEART
LOWER JAW

TYPICAL SHARK

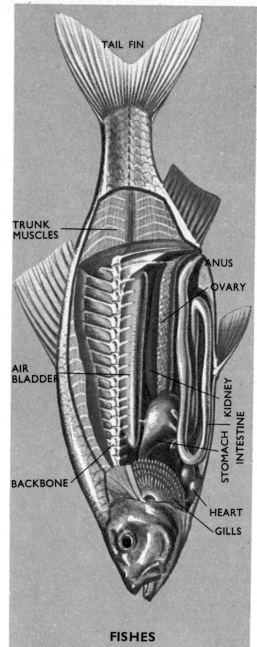

TAIL FIN

TRUNK
MUSCLES

ANUS

OVARY

AIR
BLADDER

KIDNEY

STOMACH

INTESTINE

BACKBONE

HEART

GILLS

FISHES

A fish is beautifully adapted for living in water. It has a bony *internal* skeleton. The bones move on one another at joints, and are worked by muscles attached to their outer surfaces. The bulk of the muscles are the ∑-shaped trunk muscles. They contract on alternate sides of the body from the front to the rear, bending the body in a moving wave that pushes against the water and forces the fish forwards. Fishes use their fins for braking, making sharp turns and varying their depth in the water. But they also possess an air bladder for maintaining their depth. This is a long, hollow sac inside the body cavity just above the gut. Parts of the bladder can release oxygen gas into its interior. This makes the fish buoyant and so it rises in the water. Other parts can remove the oxygen gas, when necessary, making the fish less buoyant so that it sinks.

The breathing organs (gills) take up oxygen that is dissolved in the water. It is carried round the body in the blood. The gut is a long tube with openings at both ends, and waste materials are removed by kidneys. A fish has an outer protective covering of scales.

Most fishes have an internal skeleton mainly composed of bone. The bony fishes include the teleosts, lung-fishes, and several surviving primitive forms such as the bichir, gar-pike and the sturgeons (in the latter, bone is very much reduced and the skeleton is almost wholly made of cartilage). In shape the typical teleost (e.g. salmon) is more streamlined than the cartilage fishes, being more flattened from side to side. The tail is usually symmetrical. The paired fins are small and have supporting rays. The scales are thin and flat, not tooth-like as in sharks. The mouth is larger and the lower jaw more mobile than that of sharks. The gills are covered by a flap, the operculum, and the skull has a complicated structure. The jaws are made up of several bones. The vertebral column is better developed than in sharks and bears more prominent ribs. Thin protective pads (the remains of the notochord) occur between each vertebra. A feature not found in sharks is the air bladder – an air-filled sac used as a 'floating' device. The brain is better developed than in sharks.

The gar-pike is primitive in appearance – it has a thick covering of scales.

The bichir, *Polypterus*, is a bony fish in which the body is covered with thick over-lapping and diamond-shaped (rhomboid) scales. There are many more bones in the skull than in teleosts. The air sacs (lungs) are paired like those of four-limbed animals (e.g. mammals).

The lung-fishes have a bony internal skeleton. Modern forms have no vertebrae; the notochord is present as a long rod. The paired fins are fleshy. The lungs are divided into pouches. They play an important part in respiration, the blood supply to the gills being reduced. There are internal and external openings to the nostrils. (In the other bony fishes and sharks the nostrils are not in communication with the mouth.)

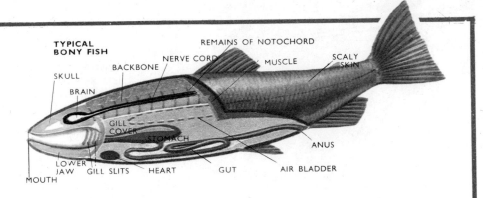

TYPICAL BONY FISH

SKULL — BRAIN — BACKBONE — NERVE CORD — REMAINS OF NOTOCHORD — MUSCLE — SCALY SKIN — GILL COVER — STOMACH — ANUS — MOUTH — LOWER JAW — GILL SLITS — HEART — GUT — AIR BLADDER

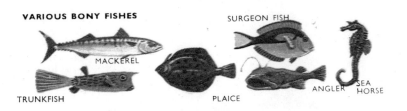

VARIOUS BONY FISHES

MACKEREL — TRUNKFISH — PLAICE — SURGEON FISH — ANGLER — SEA HORSE

There is a considerable range of size and form in teleosts – the varying position of the paired fins is of use in classification.

GAR-PIKE

Today, the gar-pike (illustrated) and the bowfin are the only two forms of the group Holostei. They have air bladders which are sacs opening off the gut.

BICHIR

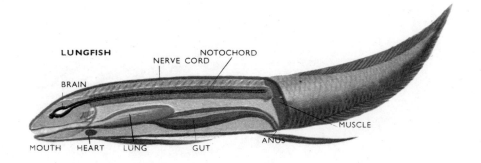

LUNGFISH

BRAIN — NERVE CORD — NOTOCHORD — MUSCLE — MOUTH — HEART — LUNG — GUT — ANUS

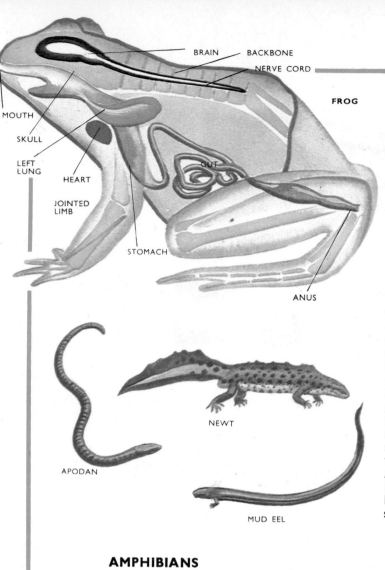

FROG

BRAIN — BACKBONE

NERVE CORD

MOUTH

SKULL

LEFT LUNG

HEART

GUT

JOINTED LIMB

STOMACH

ANUS

In contrast to fishes, amphibians (e.g. frogs, newts) have a smooth scaleless skin (except for some limbless forms). It is used for respiration. The paired limbs are jointed structures, and though the basic number of fingers is five, many amphibians have less than this. Living on land their body has to be supported (the weight of water-dwelling creatures is supported by the water), and the backbone acts as a girder transmitting the weight to the four legs. When moving quickly, newts wriggle in a way which resembles that of fishes, but slow movement is brought about by the movement of the legs, the body being raised up off the ground. In frogs the skeleton and musculature are specialised for jumping and swimming – the number of vertebrae is much reduced. Adult frogs have paired lungs. Only the tadpoles have gills, though some adult salamanders retain their gills.

NEWT

APODAN

MUD EEL

AMPHIBIANS

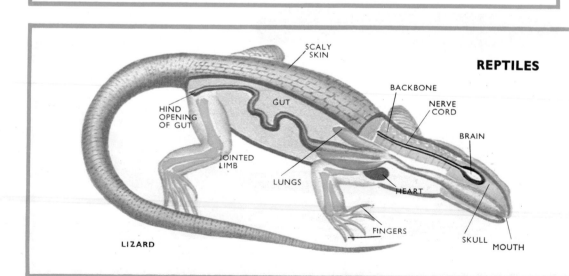

SCALY SKIN

REPTILES

BACKBONE

NERVE CORD

HIND OPENING OF GUT

GUT

BRAIN

JOINTED LIMB

LUNGS

HEART

FINGERS

SKULL MOUTH

LIZARD

BIRDS

their characteristics, page 14

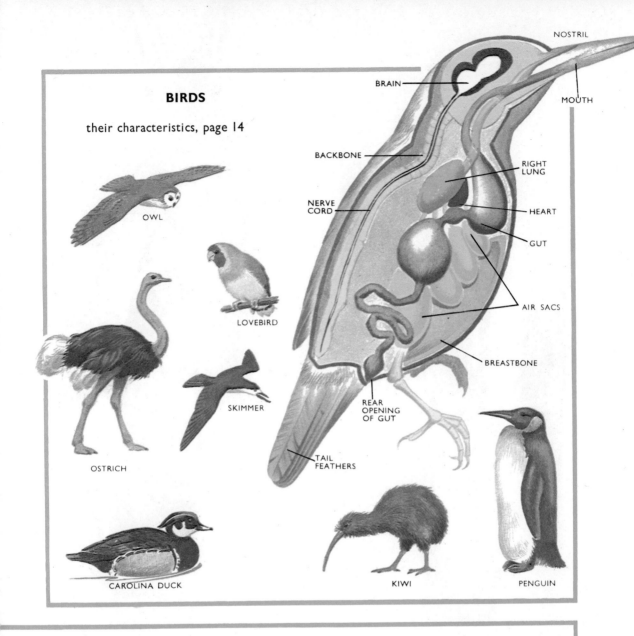

OWL

LOVEBIRD

SKIMMER

OSTRICH

CAROLINA DUCK

NOSTRIL

BRAIN

MOUTH

BACKBONE

RIGHT LUNG

NERVE CORD

HEART

GUT

AIR SACS

BREASTBONE

REAR OPENING OF GUT

TAIL FEATHERS

KIWI

PENGUIN

Reptiles have a scaly skin. The forelimbs are jointed and typically five-fingered (though limbs are absent in snakes). They all breathe air by means of lungs and breed on land, laying shelled eggs (amphibians have to return to water to breed). The head is held off the ground and the neck is better developed than in amphibians, though the plan of the skeleton is similar to that of amphibians. Ribs are well developed between the shoulder and hip regions. Reptiles have more powerful jaws than amphibians.

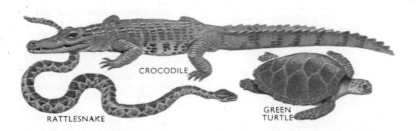

CROCODILE

RATTLESNAKE

GREEN TURTLE

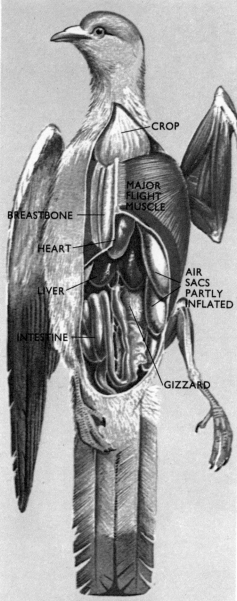

CROP

MAJOR FLIGHT MUSCLE

BREASTBONE

HEART

LIVER

AIR SACS PARTLY INFLATED

INTESTINE

GIZZARD

TAIL FEATHERS

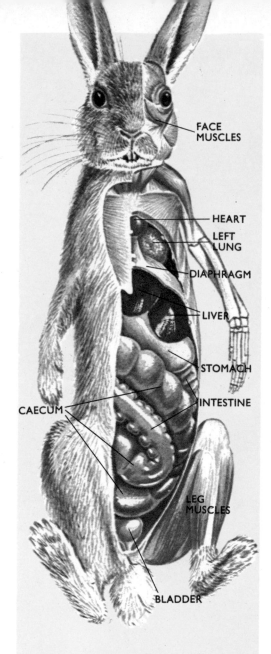

FACE MUSCLES

HEART

LEFT LUNG

DIAPHRAGM

LIVER

STOMACH

INTESTINE

CAECUM

LEG MUSCLES

BLADDER

BIRDS

Just as a fish is designed for life in water so a bird is designed for flying. A bird has a bony, *internal* skeleton. Many of the bones are hollow to reduce the bird's weight for flying. Like humans, a bird has ribs. These form a protective cage round the heart and lungs. The backbone and shoulder and hip girdles are designed so that the weight of the body is carried on the wings in flying and on the legs in walking. The large flight muscles may account for one-fifth of the total body weight and are attached to a large, keeled breastbone and the upper part of the wing.

A bird has large air sacs in the spaces in its body and even in the hollow bones. They are filled with the air which passes through the lungs when the bird breathes in and are emptied through the lungs when the bird breathes out, so the lungs constantly receive the large quantities of oxygen that are needed for flying.

Birds, like mammals, are warm-blooded. They have no teeth but a tough, horny beak. The food is not chewed but it is stored in the crop after it is swallowed and is later ground up in the muscular gizzard which may contain stones.

MAMMALS

Mammals have a bony *internal* skeleton. The bones and muscles of the legs carry the whole weight of the body while the backbone is a 'girder' between them from which the gut and other organs hang. The legs themselves are levers worked by the leg muscles and, by their movements, the animal is able to move from one place to another, often at great speed. In the rabbit, the hind legs are long and provide the drive for hopping. In large mammals, too, such as horses, the hind legs provide the drive for running while the front legs take the weight. As in birds, the rib cage protects the lungs and heart, but an important difference is the separation of these organs from the organs in the lower part of the body (abdomen) by a thin sheet of muscle – the diaphragm. This, with the ribs and their muscles, works to enlarge the chest, so drawing air into the lungs, and, to reduce its size, so forcing air out. In most mammals the diaphragm moves backwards and forwards but in humans it moves up and down because the body is upright. Mammals are warm-blooded and have a covering of hair which helps to reduce heat loss through the skin.

MAMMALS

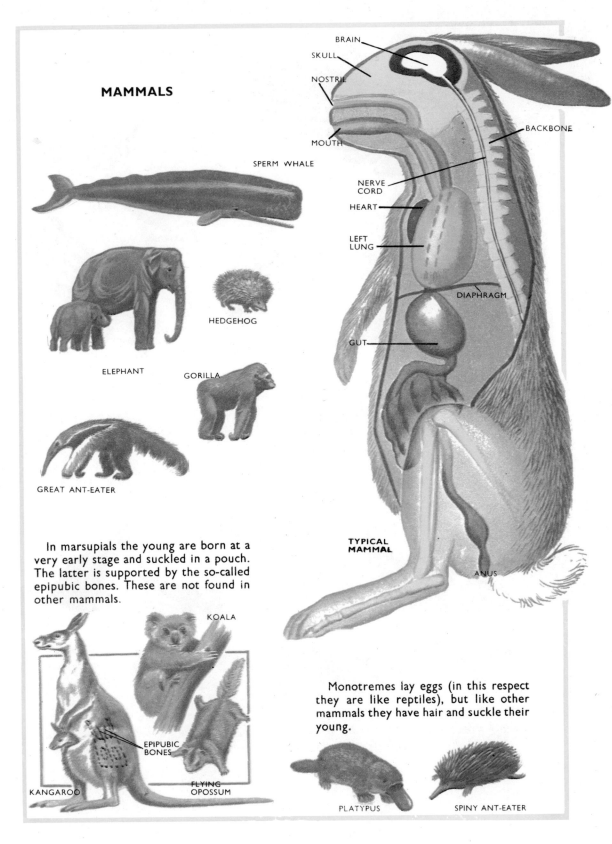

SPERM WHALE

ELEPHANT

HEDGEHOG

GORILLA

GREAT ANT-EATER

BRAIN

SKULL

NOSTRIL

MOUTH

NERVE CORD

HEART

LEFT LUNG

BACKBONE

DIAPHRAGM

GUT

TYPICAL MAMMAL

ANUS

In marsupials the young are born at a very early stage and suckled in a pouch. The latter is supported by the so-called epipubic bones. These are not found in other mammals.

KOALA

EPIPUBIC BONES

KANGAROO

FLYING OPOSSUM

Monotremes lay eggs (in this respect they are like reptiles), but like other mammals they have hair and suckle their young.

PLATYPUS

SPINY ANT-EATER

Labels on anatomical diagram: PECTORALIS MINOR, HUMERUS, PECTORALIS MAJOR, KEEL OF BREASTBONE

The power stroke in bird flight is the downward stroke. The wing is brought downward by the large pectoralis major muscle of the breast. This muscle is by far the largest in the body. (see page 25)

The Physiology
of Vertebrates

CHAPTER TWO

The Skeleton

MOST animals have a skeleton. In backboneless or invertebrate animals (insects, crabs, snails, etc.) that have a skeleton, it is usually a hard outer or *exoskeleton*. In backboned or vertebrate animals (fishes, birds, mammals etc.) the skeleton is a hard inner or *endoskeleton*.

Movement in all but the very simple animals is carried out by muscles which lengthen or shorten. In order to do this they must have some firm support or anchorage (in much the same way as the cable lengthening and shortening on the jib of a crane to move it would not work without the rigid parts of the crane to act as anchorage and levers). Such anchorage in an animal is provided by the skeleton.

In addition, if an animal is at all bulky, it requires some framework or system of rigid girders on which the soft parts of the body can be hung to prevent the whole mass from collapsing in a heap. Animals which live in water need only comparatively light skeletons, for water is dense enough to provide a large amount of support (unlike air which cannot do so). If the animal lives on land it must support its own weight and there must be some parts rigid enough and strong enough to carry its whole weight over the ground.

Some idea of the size of bones necessary for a really large land animal can be gained from the fossil skeletons of the dinosaur *Brontosaurus*. This massive creature, some 80 feet long, had limb bones about a foot thick. Yet it is almost certain that *Brontosaurus* lived in shallow water and waded about, its weight largely supported by the water, for even bones this thick would not have been strong enough to support the whole of its great weight.

A whale has, for its great weight, a very light skeleton; but a whale spends all its life in water and the water supports its weight. When a whale is stranded on the shore, however, such is its huge weight that the lungs are compressed and the whale, being unable to breathe, may suffocate. (Unlike land mammals the whale does not have a strong rib-cage or limbs to prop it up.)

Since the skeleton must be made of some rigid or tough material, it can also protect vital organs against damage; the braincase of the skull, the backbone surrounding the spinal cord and the ribs and breastbone round the heart and lungs are examples of this.

The hard outer shell (exoskeleton) of an insect obviously gives the insect its shape, but even when the skeleton is internal it still determines the basic shape of an animal. Our skull, for example, is very different in shape from that of a dog's, the neck of a giraffe is not like ours in proportion even though it contains the same number of bones (called vertebrae).

The skeletons of all vertebrates are made of bone or cartilage or both. The main axis of the skeleton is the backbone to which are attached the girdles (shoulders and hips) from which the limb bones articulate, the skull and the rib cage.

Bones meet at *joints*. The type of

joint depends on the amount of movement that there is between the bones which make the joint. The skull, for example, is made up of a number of bones. These move very little on each other. They are separated by thin layers of connective tissue which form the so-called *sutures*. Where there is a little more movement, as between the bones (vertebrae) of the backbone (vertebral column), a pad of gristle joins the bones together.

When the bones move freely on each other, as at the knee, hip, shoulder or elbow, the smooth ends of the bones are covered in a thin layer of cartilage. A connective tissue capsule holds the bones together. The inner part of the capsule forms what is called the *synovial membrane*. This produces a lubricating fluid, the *synovial fluid*. The cartilage, besides reducing the friction between the bones, also acts as a shock absorber so that the bones do not split or shatter when they take severe stresses at the joints (as when a parachutist makes a landing).

The knee is a hinged joint, for the bones move on each other in a similar way to the two parts of a hinge. The leg forms a ball-and-socket joint with the hip. The rounded end of the thigh bone (femur) fits into a socket in the hip girdle.

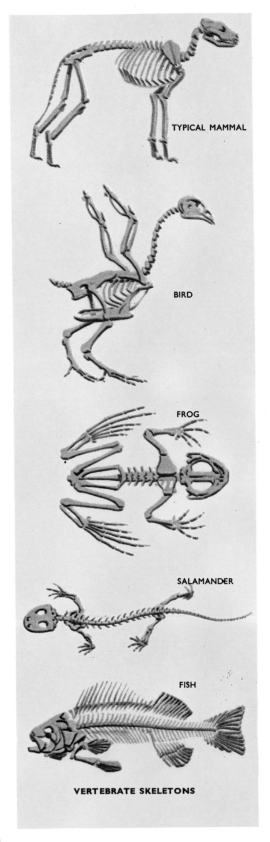

TYPICAL MAMMAL

BIRD

FROG

SALAMANDER

FISH

VERTEBRATE SKELETONS

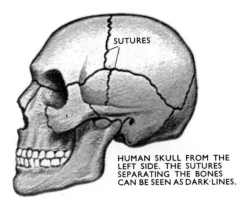

SUTURES

HUMAN SKULL FROM THE LEFT SIDE. THE SUTURES SEPARATING THE BONES CAN BE SEEN AS DARK LINES.

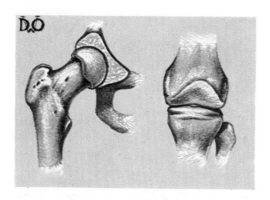

(Left) *The human hip joint showing how the ball of the thigh bone fits into the socket on the hip girdle.* (Right) *The human knee, a hinge joint.*

The construction of the bones is such that they are able to withstand the stresses to which they are subjected. The upper third of the thigh bone, for example, is stronger than the lower part, for it has to withstand the greatest stress in this region. In cross-section it is hollow. When a bone is subjected to bending stresses the forces operating on it are greatest at its outside so that the hollow represents a great saving in bone building material, and compared with a solid structure it makes the bone lighter so that the work of the muscles is made much easier. In a similar way engineers reduce the weight and the amount of materials used in building such structures as cranes and bridges by using girders which are I-shaped or are made up of a number of short rods or members (see illustration) joined together in such a way that the strength of the girder is the same. The hollow frame of a bicycle is just as strong as a solid one would be and, of course, much lighter. The muscles, too, are arranged in such a way that the stresses on the bones are considerably reduced.

The bones in the body act as levers which are operated by the muscles. There are three main kinds of levers (first, second or third order) depending on the positions of the pulling force, on the position of the weight which is being lifted and on where the lever is pivoted (fulcrum). The load (weight) lifted divided by the effort or force is called the *mechanical advantage* of the lever. Most muscles work at a mechanical disadvantage; the pull is exerted very much closer to the fulcrum than the weight is.

The illustrations show an example of each of the orders of levers in

Part of a wing bone from a vulture showing the internal strutting similar in construction to an aeroplane wing (right). The bone is able to take stresses as well as it would if it were solid and the saving in weight is of great advantage to the bird in flying.

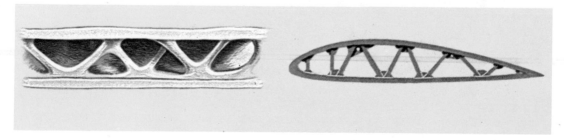

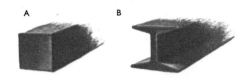

Engineers could use shape A for a girder but in fact use B which is just as strong and consumes less material.

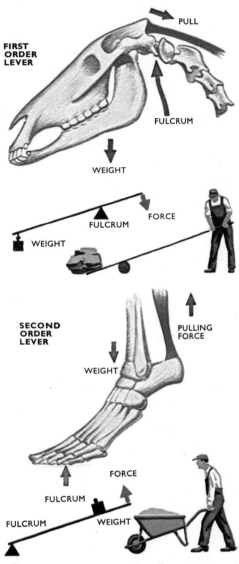

FIRST ORDER LEVER

PULL

FULCRUM

WEIGHT

FULCRUM

FORCE

WEIGHT

SECOND ORDER LEVER

WEIGHT

PULLING FORCE

FULCRUM

FORCE

FULCRUM

WEIGHT

animal bodies. The horse's head is an example of a lever of the first order because the fulcrum is between the weight and the force. The human foot is an example of a lever of the second order since the weight is between the fulcrum and the force, and the human elbow is an example of a third order lever as the pulling force is between the fulcrum and the weight. Of these three examples the calf muscles, which enable us to stand on our toes, are the only ones to work at a mechanical advantage. In negroes, who have a longer heel than whites, the calf muscles work at a greater mechanical advantage.

The hollow parts of a bicycle frame are just as strong as they would be were they solid.

THIRD ORDER LEVER

PULLING FORCE

FULCRUM

WEIGHT

WEIGHT

FORCE

FULCRUM

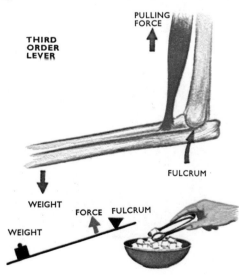

21

CHAPTER THREE

Muscles and Movement

MUSCLE tissue accounts for more than one third of the weight of the typical vertebrate body. Most of this muscle is skeletal muscle – attached to the skeleton and forming the flesh of the animal. Skeletal muscle is responsible for the movement of an animal – of almost all animals, not just the vertebrates.

Under the microscope, skeletal muscle is seen to be composed of bundles of long, tapering cells crossed by numerous light and dark stripes. It is thus also called striped muscle. When stimulated by a nerve impulse, muscle tissue can contract very strongly and it is this property that produces movement. As explained in the last chapter, the bones act as levers acted upon by muscles. The muscles are attached to the bones on each side of a joint. Contraction of a muscle produces movement of one bone against the other. For example, the biceps of the arm joins the upper arm to the fore-arm across the front of the elbow. When the biceps contracts it pulls the fore-arm up to-

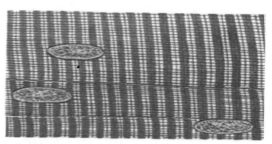

A highly magnified view of striped muscle.

wards the upper arm. The triceps muscle joins the same two bones, but across the back of the elbow. When it contracts it pulls the arm straight again. As the triceps contracts the biceps relaxes and returns to its uncontracted position. A contracted muscle cannot extend itself – it must be stretched out by an opposing muscle.

Skeletal muscle is under conscious control and can act very quickly when necessary. It therefore has yet another alternative name – voluntary muscle. Although skeletal muscle can contract very quickly, it is quick to tire and cannot remain contracted for very long periods.

Balloons in a model show the working of the main muscles which raise and lower the human arm. When a muscle contracts its volume does not change.

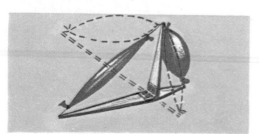

The attachment of a muscle to a bone through a tendon. A muscle may be made up of several large bundles of muscle fibres, each bundle composed of smaller bundles of fibres.

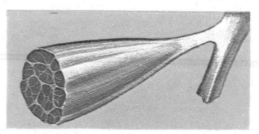

The skeletal muscles of all vertebrates are constructed on the same pattern, although their arrangement in the body varies considerably according to the types of limb and the types of movement of the animal concerned.

Other Types of Muscle

Although skeletal muscle is the commonest type of muscle in the body, there are two other very important types. One of these is cardiac or heart muscle. It is found only in the heart. The fibres are joined together to form a sort of network but are otherwise similar to those of skeletal muscle. Cardiac muscle is able to contract rhythmically and, most important, *without tiring*. The heart could not possibly be composed of ordinary skeletal muscle when it has to beat many times every second for maybe more than 100 years.

The third type of muscle is called smooth muscle. It is found in the

The long hind legs of a frog give increased leverage in jumping.

gut wall, in the linings of the lungs and blood vessels, and also in the iris of the eye. The cells are not aggregated into bundles in the same way as the cells of striped muscle – they are held together in sheets by connective tissues. The striped pattern of skeletal muscle is not seen in smooth muscle, which is therefore

---

Each unstriped muscle fibre is about $\frac{1}{5}$th millimetre long and $\frac{1}{150}$th millimetre wide and has a central nucleus. The fibre tapers to a point at each end. Smooth muscle is capable of slow, sustained contractions such as those that are needed to push the food slowly through the gut.

Each striped muscle fibre is about $\frac{1}{10}$th millimetre in diameter and may be several centimetres long. Each contains hundreds of nuclei and is made of long, thin strands or fibrils which appear striped with alternate light and dark bands. The width of these bands alters when the muscle contracts.

Cardiac muscle is found only in the wall of the heart. It is composed of fibres which branch and join to form an elaborate network. This arrangement is fitted for the muscle movement needed to enlarge and shrink the bag-shaped heart. The fibres are made up of fibrils and these are striped in a similar way to those of striped muscle. At intervals dark bands or partitions cross the fibres.

Muscle Cells

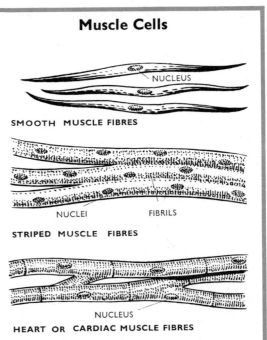

NUCLEUS

SMOOTH MUSCLE FIBRES

NUCLEI   FIBRILS

STRIPED MUSCLE FIBRES

NUCLEUS

HEART OR CARDIAC MUSCLE FIBRES

also called unstriped muscle. The function of smooth muscle is to control the movement of the gut and the passage of food along it, and also to control the size of the blood vessels, according to the demand for blood by any particular region of the body. Such functions are not performed consciously and smooth mus-

(below) The z-shaped muscles of a bony fish. In a fish the fibres within the muscle blocks contract and cause the body to bend.

backbone. The bulk of the muscles are body muscles. However, in the higher vertebrates (particularly birds and mammals) the limb muscles provide movement so that the role of the body muscles is reduced. In shark-like fishes forward movement is produced by contraction of the muscle fibres which are arranged lengthwise in each block. If the fibres in any one block contract the result is a bending of the body. To produce forward movement fibres in each muscle block contract in one block after another from the front of the fish to the rear so that waves pass backwards down the body, producing a backward thrust on the water. The waves occur alternately on each side of the fish. Rapid production of these

cle is thus also called involuntary muscle. It does not contract nearly so fast as does skeletal muscle but it is able to hold its contracted state for a long period. For example, in bright sunlight, the pupil of the eye gets smaller and remains so as long as conditions are the same. Smooth muscle is responsible for this maintenance. Smooth muscle also controls the ducts leading from various glands.

Movement

Typically in vertebrates (e.g. fishes) the striped muscles are arranged in a series of blocks on either side of the

can produce very fast movement through the water. The tail fin produces much of the forward motion and, with the pectoral fins, keeps the fish at the same level in the water.

When a wave passes down one side of the body only, the fish is able to make very sharp turns. In bony fishes movement of the paired fins (they have small muscles to move them) may also enable the fish to turn and they may also assist braking.

In nearly all four-footed animals (tetrapods) each limb has three main joints. These are the shoulder, elbow and wrist in the forelimbs, and the hip, knee and ankle in the hind-limbs. The muscles are so arranged that the limbs can be moved backwards and forwards by the muscles between them and the shoulder and hip girdle. They can also be bent and extended by their own muscles and twisted or rotated, movements which are often very important for the exact

A lizard bends its body in a similar way to a fish, though not to the same extent.

placing of the limbs in walking and running.

The salamander, when swimming, wriggles its body in a similar manner to fishes. When it walks on land the legs hold the body off the ground and are used as levers moved by the muscles. Frogs have long hind legs which provide for increased leverage in jumping.

In lizards there is less bending of the body than in salamanders. The head is also held high off the ground. But in most respects the method of locomotion is very similar. The legs are thrown out to the side as the animal moves forward. This contrasts with movement in most mammals where the limbs are held under the body and moved straight forward.

Most snakes crawl by moving the body in a series of side-to-side curves, much as a fish does. In the same way that the back of each curve in the fish's body pushes against the water,

so the back of each curve in the snake's body pushes against the ground, and so moves the snake forward. This can be shown by placing a snake on ground which has a light covering of sand. The sand is thrown into a series of piles, each pile marking the backward push of a curve of the body. The scales on the underside of the snake's body aid the snake in moving. Each has a muscle which can erect it and so help to prevent the snake from sliding backwards.

Birds are the most successful of flying creatures, though a few, such as the ostrich, are flightless and use their powerful legs for fast running. The skeleton is so designed that the weight of the body is carried on the wings in flying and on the legs in walking. The flight muscles are relatively huge and may themselves account for one fifth of the total body weight. They are attached to a large, keeled breastbone and the upper part of the wing. The main flight muscle (pectoralis major) runs from the breastbone to the underside of the bone (humerus) in the upper part of the wing. Its fibres are red in birds that are strong flyers. Contraction of the pectoralis major lowers the wing. Raising of the wing is produced by a smaller muscle, the pectoralis minor, which runs beneath the pectoralis major from the breastbone to the upper side of the humerus. Other smaller shoulder muscles help to twist the wing and move it into other positions, lowering its hind edge or varying the position of its leading edge – movements which are of great importance in flying. The muscles of the arm itself fold the wing or keep it extended.

Bats are the only mammals which

are capable of sustained flight. The wing is a membrane which stretches from the long forearm along the side of the body and envelops the hind limbs. It is supported by four of the fingers which have become enormously elongated. The flight muscles, attached to the keel of the breastbone and the forearm, are quite large.

Most mammals run about on all fours. The legs are characteristically moved straight backwards and forwards underneath the body. In man both the arms and legs are able to move freely in other directions, though there is more movement at the shoulder than at the hip joint.

In hoofed animals, such as horses, the limbs are lengthened by raising them on the toes. During their evolution some toes have been lost; more usually only one or two remain forming the axis of the limb. Movement is restricted to a fore-and-aft direction, but the arrangement of the joints and the limb muscles makes for very fast running. The hind limbs provide most of the drive, while the fore-limbs play the role of weight-bearers.

Many hoofed mammals live in grassland plains where fast movement is both possible and necessary in order to avoid the attentions of the big cats which prey on them. In the cats the skeleton and the muscles are specialised for making the quick leaps with which prey are captured. Much of the weight of the long body is carried on the front limbs and the tail is used as a balancing organ.

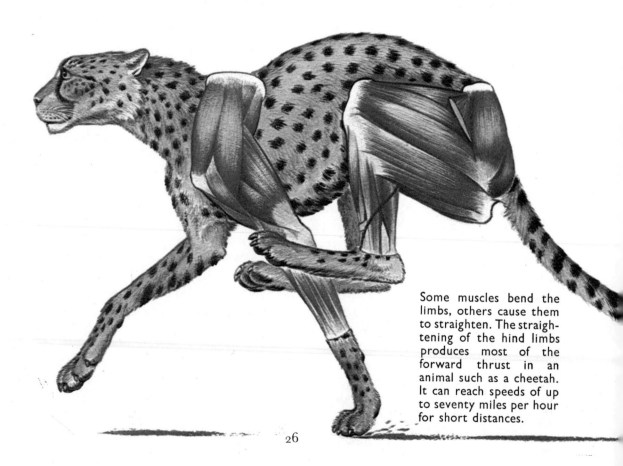

Some muscles bend the limbs, others cause them to straighten. The straightening of the hind limbs produces most of the forward thrust in an animal such as a cheetah. It can reach speeds of up to seventy miles per hour for short distances.

26

CHAPTER FOUR

Feeding and Digestion

THE feeding habits of vertebrates vary enormously. Many fishes merely swallow the tiny particles or organisms that they find floating in the water. Even the huge blue whale – the largest living animal – feeds by straining tiny planktonic creatures from the water. The carnivores hunt their prey and, having caught it, tear it to pieces with their teeth and claws. The hoofed animals browse or graze on vegetation which they rip off with their teeth. There are many other feeding habits and in every case the mouths and teeth are admirably suited for the job. The various shapes of birds' beaks are good examples of this. Another example is shown by the white and black rhinoceros species. The white rhino is a grazing animal and its wide, blunt snout is well suited to this way of feeding. The black rhino on the other hand feeds by browsing on shrubs. Its snout is far more pointed than that of the white rhino and the upper lip is able to pull branches into the mouth.

When once food has been obtained and passed to the mouth it follows a very similar path in all vertebrates. Later chapters will show that the digestive system varies a little from

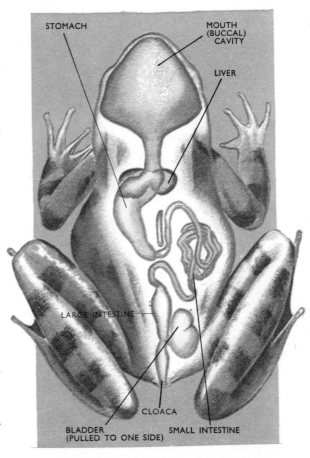

STOMACH

MOUTH (BUCCAL) CAVITY

LIVER

LARGE INTESTINE

BLADDER (PULLED TO ONE SIDE)

CLOACA

SMALL INTESTINE

Amphibians

The gut of amphibians, such as the frog, is very much as described though there are no salivary glands and no digestion takes place in the mouth. Adult frogs live mainly on insects, flicking out the sticky tongue which is attached to the floor of the mouth.

group to group but the basic plan is recognisable in all vertebrates.

The mouth – usually containing a number of teeth – is the first part of the alimentary canal or gut. The teeth help to hold the food and in mammals they break it up into small lumps. The mouth may also contain salivary glands which pour liquid on to the food. Preliminary breakdown of starch may take place in the mouth.

From the mouth, the small pieces of food pass down the oesophagus and into the stomach. The latter is a large 'bag' in which the food is churned up with a large volume of liquid. This liquid contains hydrochloric acid and two enzymes – rennin which clots milk, and pepsin which breaks down protein. After a time in the stomach, the food is reduced to a thick liquid. It then passes, by way of a valve, into the small intestine. The walls of this part of the gut produce enzymes. Ducts from the pancreas and the gall bladder join into the small intestine. All the juices added to the food help to break it down further – proteins are finally reduced to amino-acids, starches and sugars into simple sugar molecules, and fats into glycerol and fatty acids. These small molecules are then able to pass through the walls of the small intestine and into the blood stream to be carried to the parts of the body where they are needed. The small intestine is relatively long and ensures that all the food material is absorbed on its way through the gut.

The enzymes produced in the gut are able to deal with the varied diets of all vertebrates but plant material needs more specialised treatment. The guts of plant-eating animals are relatively longer than those of meat-eaters and more specialised in parts. The plant-eating tadpole, for example, has a longer and more complicated gut than the adult frog.

After the small intestine, the food – although by now there is little actual food in it – reaches the large intestine or colon. The main function of this region is to reabsorb all the valuable water that has been poured on to the food during the earlier stages of digestion. The undigested material then passes out through the rectum as the faeces.

CHAPTER FIVE

Breathing

PROTOZOANS get oxygen by simple diffusion from the surroundings. Coelenterates are also able to maintain their rather sluggish activity without special respiratory organs. Earthworms absorb their oxygen requirements through the skin which is very well supplied with blood vessels. This arrangement is possible only in damp surroundings. In dry air, water would very rapidly be lost through the skin. All larger or more active animals have special respiratory organs to absorb oxygen. Animals living in water usually have *gills* to absorb oxygen from the water. Land vertebrates usually breathe (i.e. take in air) by means of *lungs*. Insects and some other arthropods have a network of tubes (*tracheae*) throughout the body. These conduct air from the surroundings to every part of the body.

The essential features of respiratory organs are: a large moist surface area, very thin walls, and a good blood supply. The gills of fishes and of crustaceans consist of very thin plates of tissue over which water is caused to pass by various movements of the animal. Oxygen, dissolved in the water, passes into the blood stream and is transported to the tissues. Because a stream of water flows over the gills there is always a fresh source of oxygen next to the gill. Lungs are internal chambers with no continuous air-flow. They have to be filled and emptied by breathing movements. The lungs open to the outside by way of the *bronchi* and the *trachea* (windpipe). Each lung is made up of

---

Blood pigments

There are a number of blood pigments of which the best known is *haemoglobin*—the reddish purple pigment of vertebrate blood and of some invertebrates (e.g. earthworms). This is a complex iron-containing compound which occurs in the corpuscles of vertebrate blood or in the plasma in other animals. At high oxygen concentrations (e.g. at the respiratory surface) the pigment combines with oxygen and forms *oxyhaemoglobin* which is bright red. In the body tissues the oxygen concentration is low. The oxyhaemoglobin in the blood breaks down and releases oxygen which passes to the tissues. If the haemoglobin content is reduced, oxygen shortage will occur. For example, carbon monoxide forms a stable compound—*carboxyhaemoglobin*—with the pigment which cannot then carry oxygen. Other pigments occur in some animals. *Haemocyanin*, in which the metallic element is copper, is found in crustaceans and molluscs such as octopuses and squids. It turns blue when oxygenated. All respiratory pigments have in common the fact that they form unstable compounds with oxygen which break down at the low oxygen concentration found in the tissues.

---

thousands of tiny air-sacs (*alveoli*) which link together and lead to the bronchi. The alveoli are lined with a thin layer of mucus and on the outside are covered with a network of fine blood capillaries. When air is breathed out, the lung is not completely emptied. A good deal of residual air remains in the alveoli. Oxygen from fresh air breathed in has to diffuse through this residual air and through the mucus before reaching the thin wall of the alveolus. To overcome this disadvantage the total surface is very large—much larger than the corresponding gill surface would need to be.

Absorption of oxygen into the blood follows the same pattern in lungs and in gills. In both cases the oxygen is in solution when it reaches the respiratory surface. The blood arriving here is low in oxygen content and thus the oxygen outside passes in solution through the thin walls and into the blood which transports it to the tissues. Only a very small amount of the oxygen is carried as a simple solution in the blood. Most of it combines with a *respiratory pigment* in the blood. The compound formed is unstable and later releases oxygen in the capillaries of the body. In the body the tissues are low in oxygen content so that the oxygen released passes through the fine capillary walls and into the cells where the chemical reactions take place. These reactions are very complicated and involve numerous enzymes and intermediate stages. The net result, however, can be shown as:

food + oxygen = carbon dioxide + water + energy

This equation holds good for both plants and animals. Glucose is a commonly used food material. Its oxidation can be shown chemically as follows:

$$C_6H_{12}O_6 + 6O_2 = 6CO_2 + 6H_2O + energy$$
(glucose) (oxygen)(carbon dioxide) (water)

Most of the carbon dioxide released is removed by the blood stream. Some is carried in solution and some in combination with blood proteins, but by far the largest amount is carried in the form of bicarbonate ions. In the blood capillaries of the tissues carbon dioxide and water combine to form carbonic acid:

$$CO_2 + H_2O \rightleftharpoons H_2CO_3$$

This then breaks down into ions:

$$H_2CO_3 \rightleftharpoons H^+ + HCO_3^-.$$

At the respiratory surface the blood becomes more acid (due to the formation of oxyhaemoglobin) and the bicarbonates are broken down, releasing carbon dioxide which passes through the respiratory surface and out to the surroundings.

THE HISTORY OF THE LUNG

It is generally accepted that the tetrapods – the basically four-footed land vertebrates – arose from fish-like ancestors. The fins gradually evolved into five-fingered limbs enabling the creatures to move about on land, but perhaps even more interesting was the change-over from gill-breathing to lung-breathing.

The ancestral tetrapods did not suddenly develop lungs when they started to come out on land. Evidence suggests that they possessed simple lungs long before that – when they were still firmly in the 'fishy stage'.

There are alive today a number of strange fishes which, although they have gills, breathe largely by gulping air into pouches very similar to the

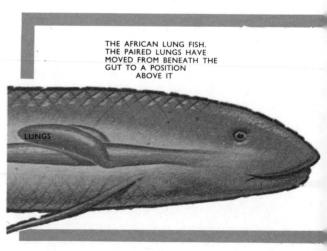

THE AFRICAN LUNG FISH. THE PAIRED LUNGS HAVE MOVED FROM BENEATH THE GUT TO A POSITION ABOVE IT

LUNGS

lungs of tetrapods. Their gills are rather inefficient. Three of these fishes are the so-called 'lung-fishes' – survivors of the group which long ago gave rise to the land vertebrates. Another of the air-breathing fishes is the bichir (*Polypterus*) of certain African rivers. The bichir is a surviving member of the group which gave rise to the modern fishes and, despite the similarities of the lungs, the bichir is not closely related to the lung-fishes. The lung-fishes have fleshy lobes in their fins while the bichir has rayed fins like the typical modern fishes.

It is clear, then, that the primitive lung structure appeared before the two groups of fishes diverged. It probably arose first as a small pocket on the underside of the pharynx (throat). As time went by this pocket evolved into a larger and larger structure and, at least in some creatures, forked into two. The pharynx of fishes is well supplied with blood and so, presumably, would any out-

growth from it be. Thus by gulping air into these pouches the ancient fishes were able to increase the amount of oxygen they could absorb. This possibly did not matter to those fishes living in the sea, but at the time this development was going on the climate was very dry and lakes and rivers were drying up and pools were becoming stagnant. The ability to breathe air was a great advantage to the fishes. Those with fleshy lobes in their fins were able to leave drying pools and in this way the first land-living vertebrates evolved.

At first the lungs were not very efficient but with time they evolved into the efficient organs of today's vertebrates. The earliest land-living vertebrates were the amphibians and today's amphibians, although very different in most ways from the early amphibians, have rather inefficient lungs. The more complex lungs of other groups are described later in this book.

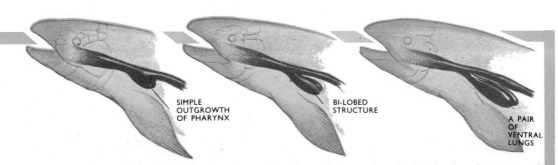

SIMPLE
OUTGROWTH
OF PHARYNX

BI-LOBED
STRUCTURE

A PAIR
OF
VENTRAL
LUNGS

Left, the African lungfish. The two lungs lie above the gut though the air duct is connected to the undersurface. Above, possibly how the lungs developed. In stagnant pools certain fish supplemented their oxygen supply by gulping air. Oxygen was absorbed first through the mouth walls, then through a downgrowth of the pharynx surface.

31

CHAPTER SIX

The Heart and Circulation

IN its main features the blood system conforms to the same basic plan in all vertebrates. As the vertebrates have evolved, changes in the blood system have taken place, some associated with the great change from breathing oxygen dissolved in water to breathing oxygen in the air. This came about when the transition from dwelling in water to living on land occurred. At the highest level in the birds and mammals we see the evolution of a high-pressure system in which a rapid circulation is maintained and in which oxygenated blood from the lungs is kept separate from deoxygenated blood that is passing to the lungs. Adequate fuel and oxygen can thus be carried to the tissues and waste materials transported away quickly. Such a system permits the continuous activity that we associate with birds and mammals.

In gill-breathing vertebrates (e.g. fishes) blood flows forwards from the *heart* along the *ventral aorta* in the floor of the throat. A series of vessels pass upwards from the ventral aorta to the gills on either side of the throat. There they break up into a fine meshwork of *capillaries* which provide a much increased surface area in contact with dissolved oxygen in the water. The capillaries rejoin to form vessels that pass upwards to join the *dorsal aorta*, along the hindpart of which blood flows back to supply the body and, in its front part, forwards to supply the head. Branches from the dorsal aorta supply the various parts of the body (e.g.

limbs, kidneys, liver and the skin).

In the tissues the arteries break down into a system of capillaries. These are so fine and form such an elaborate branching network that most of the cells are near to, or actually in contact with, a capillary. The passage of food and oxygen to the tissues and of waste materials in the opposite direction can take place quickly. If these materials had to 'seep' (diffuse) over greater distances between larger (less divided) vessels the rate at which the tissues work would be very much slower. Indeed it is doubtful if they would receive sufficient food and oxygen, for diffusion is efficient only over very short distances.

The system of *veins* (*venous system*) bringing blood from the capillary system to the heart is complicated, but basically consists of the following sets of vessels: vessels that pass from the gut to the liver (*hepatic portal system*) and the *hepatic veins* from the liver to the main veins entering the heart; the *cardinal veins* (replaced in higher forms by the *venae cavae*) that lie above the body cavity or gut

The primitive vertebrate heart consisted of four chambers.

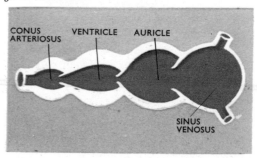

and carry blood from the back (dorsal) part of the body, the head and the limbs; veins draining the lower (ventral) part of the body wall; and, in animals with lungs, the *pulmonary veins*.

One of the most striking series of structural changes that has taken place during the course of verte-

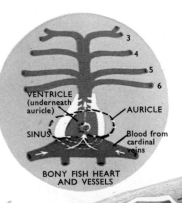

VENTRICLE (underneath auricle)
SINUS
AURICLE
Blood from cardinal veins

BONY FISH HEART AND VESSELS

DORSAL AORTA

KIDNEY

LEFT POSTERIOR CARDINAL VEIN

DORSAL AORTA

LIVER

HEPATIC VEIN

CUT END OF ANTERIOR CARDINAL VEIN

HEART

FALSE GILL

GILL CAPILLARIES

ARTERY AWAY FROM GILL (EFFERENT)

ARTERY TO GILL (AFFERENT)

VENTRAL AORTA

2 is lost

BONY FISH

33

(Hepatic portal system omitted)

brate evolution has concerned the vessels that pass from the ventral aorta to the dorsal aorta—the so-called *aortic arch system*.

In the embryos of vertebrates six pairs of aortic arches can usually be recognised (numbered 1–6 from front to rear). They are vessels that run uninterrupted between the ventral aorta and the dorsal aorta. As the gill slits open and begin to work, a capillary system is established and so the vessel is interrupted—i.e. divided into two parts, an *afferent* part (to the gills) and an *efferent* part (away from the gills). The arches develop from the front to the back.

Fishes have gills and breathe oxygen dissolved in the water. The arches still carry blood to and from the gills. In adult fishes arch 1 remains only as the efferent part. The afferent part is lost and the spiracle is supplied with blood that is already oxygenated from the efferent part of arch 2. Thus the spiracle is not a true gill. The part of arch 1 that remains supplies the eye with blood. In most bony fishes arch 2 is lost and in tetrapods—a term which includes all amphibians, reptiles, birds and

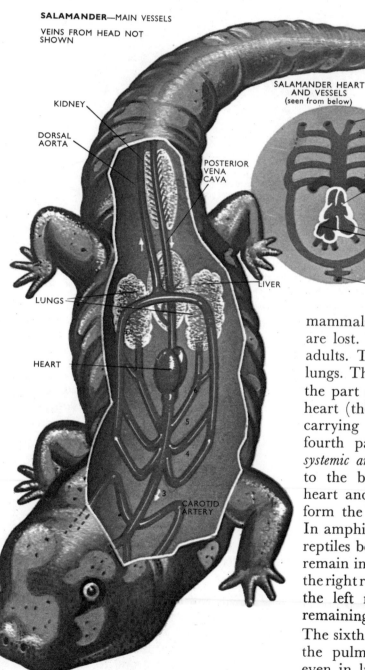

SALAMANDER—MAIN VESSELS

VEINS FROM HEAD NOT SHOWN

KIDNEY

DORSAL AORTA

POSTERIOR VENA CAVA

SALAMANDER HEART AND VESSELS (seen from below)

CAROTIDS

VENTRICLE

AURICLES

LIVER

AORTA

LUNGS

HEART

CAROTID ARTERY

mammals—the first two pairs of arches are lost. Most tetrapods lack gills as adults. They live on land and have lungs. The third pair of arches forms the part of the *carotid artery* near the heart (the carotid is the main artery carrying blood to the head). The fourth pair of arches becomes the *systemic arch* which curves backwards to the body on either side of the heart and joins behind the heart to form the vessel supplying the body. In amphibians (frogs, etc.) and most reptiles both the right and left arches remain in the adult, but in birds only the right remains and in mammals only the left remains. In mammals this remaining arch is called the aorta. The sixth pair of arches forms part of the pulmonary arteries. This is so even in lung-fishes where blood for the lungs is obtained from the sixth arch or from the aorta beyond this.

The Heart

The heart develops as a series of swellings along the main vessel passing blood from the body to the gills for reoxygenation. Primitively it con-tween the sinus and the auricle. Here the heartbeat initiates. A band of fibres (*the bundle of His*) runs from near this to the ventricle, so that contraction spreads from the auricle through to the ventricle.

This four-chambered heart is

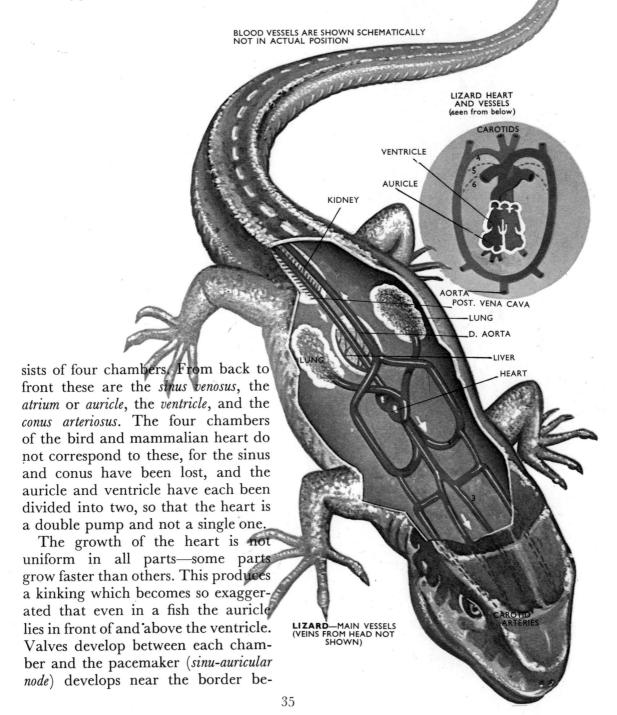

BLOOD VESSELS ARE SHOWN SCHEMATICALLY NOT IN ACTUAL POSITION

LIZARD HEART AND VESSELS (seen from below)

CAROTIDS

VENTRICLE

AURICLE

KIDNEY

AORTA
POST. VENA CAVA
LUNG
D. AORTA
LUNG
LIVER
HEART

LIZARD—MAIN VESSELS (VEINS FROM HEAD NOT SHOWN)

CAROTID ARTERIES

sists of four chambers. From back to front these are the *sinus venosus*, the *atrium* or *auricle*, the *ventricle*, and the *conus arteriosus*. The four chambers of the bird and mammalian heart do not correspond to these, for the sinus and conus have been lost, and the auricle and ventricle have each been divided into two, so that the heart is a double pump and not a single one.

The growth of the heart is not uniform in all parts—some parts grow faster than others. This produces a kinking which becomes so exaggerated that even in a fish the auricle lies in front of and above the ventricle. Valves develop between each chamber and the pacemaker (*sinu-auricular node*) develops near the border be-

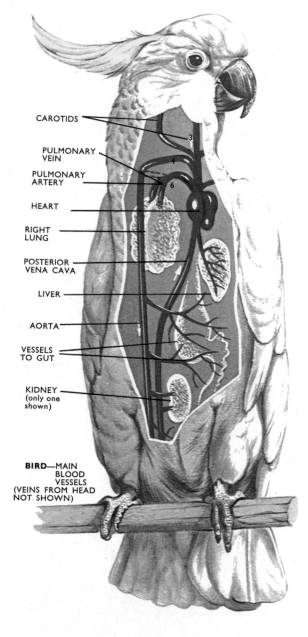

CAROTIDS

PULMONARY VEIN

PULMONARY ARTERY

HEART

RIGHT LUNG

POSTERIOR VENA CAVA

LIVER

AORTA

VESSELS TO GUT

KIDNEY (only one shown)

BIRD—MAIN BLOOD VESSELS (VEINS FROM HEAD NOT SHOWN)

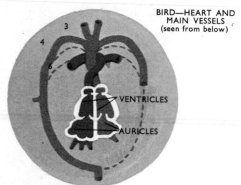

BIRD—HEART AND MAIN VESSELS (seen from below)

VENTRICLES

AURICLES

typical of shark-like fishes (in bony fishes the conus has been lost).

The sinus serves as a reservoir in which venous blood collects upon returning from the body. The auricle is thin-walled and contracts weakly. The ventricle is a powerful pump whose contraction is mainly responsible for moving the blood. The conus is muscular and provided with valves. Blood returning sluggishly in the large sinuses causes the thin-walled sinus to swell. As it contracts blood is forced into the auricle, since the valves at the hind end of the sinus close. The auricle swells and contracts, forcing blood into the ventricle and swelling it. This contracts to drive the blood forward through the gills. The pressure of blood flowing to the gills is thus gradually built up in the heart.

In both bony and shark-like fishes the blood passes through all the chambers of the heart on its way to the lungs to be oxygenated. These fish are said to have a *single circulation*. The pressure of the blood is lowered by its passage through both the gill capillaries and the capillaries in the head and body.

In land vertebrates we can follow the probable lines which the evolution of a double circulation has followed. With the development of lungs in place of gills both oxygenated blood from the former and deoxygenated blood from the body are passing into the heart together. This is an undesirable situation, for much of the oxygenation is wasted and blood passes to the body containing only a moderate amount of oxygen instead of being rich in oxygen. Obviously, then, a state of affairs is preferable where oxygenated and deoxygenated blood are kept apart. In lung-fishes, relatives of which were

36

the ancestors of land vertebrates, both the auricle and ventricle are partly divided into two and the ventral aorta is short and twisted. Its valves are arranged so that most of the blood from the left side of the auricle passes into the first two aortic arches and that from the right side passes into the hind two arches. Thus some degree of separation is obtained.

In amphibians the auricles are completely divided into two. Blood poor in oxygen that is returning from the body enters the right auricle and blood from the lungs enters the left auricle. The ventricle is not divided, but flaps of spongy tissue probably prevent complete mixing of the blood in the ventricle. In most amphibians much of the oxygen required is absorbed through the skin into the blood vessels there. Oxygenated blood from these enters the right auricle, so there is less point in keeping blood from the auricles separate in the ventricle.

In most reptiles the ventricle is almost completely divided into two. There is a slight gap in the dividing wall where the arteries to the body and lungs leave the heart so that a little mixing can take place. It is only in birds and mammals that we see a complete division of the ventricle into two and consequently complete separation of oxygenated and deoxygenated blood.

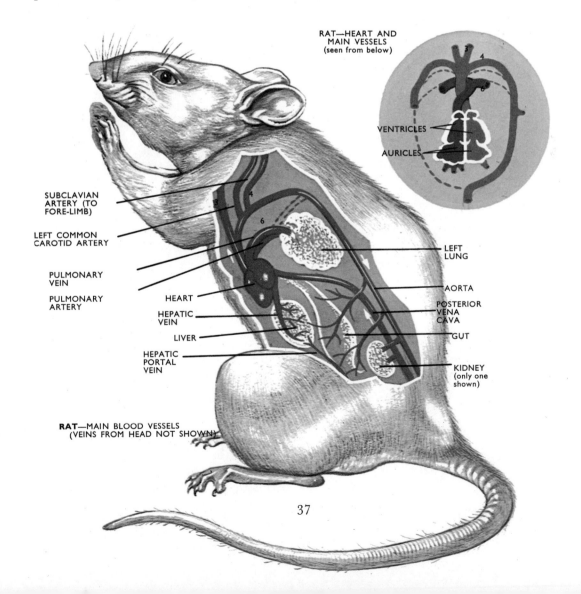

RAT—HEART AND
MAIN VESSELS
(seen from below)

VENTRICLES

AURICLES

SUBCLAVIAN
ARTERY (TO
FORE-LIMB)

LEFT COMMON
CAROTID ARTERY

PULMONARY
VEIN

PULMONARY
ARTERY

HEART

HEPATIC
VEIN

LIVER

HEPATIC
PORTAL
VEIN

LEFT
LUNG

AORTA

POSTERIOR
VENA
CAVA

GUT

KIDNEY
(only one
shown)

RAT—MAIN BLOOD VESSELS
(VEINS FROM HEAD NOT SHOWN)

37

CHAPTER SEVEN

The Excretory System

EXCRETION is the removal of waste substances from the body. These substances are largely the result of metabolic activities but also include water taken in by osmosis.

In vertebrate animals paired kidneys are the major organs of excretion. Each kidney consists of a number of tubules made up of a *capsule* and a tube. The capsule has within

A diagram of a single kidney tubule. Arrows show the direction of blood flow and the flow of urine.

it a knot of capillaries (*glomerulus*) from which water, waste and salts are driven, by the force of the heartbeat, through the capsule wall into the tubule. Various parts of the tube reabsorb water and other essential materials and thus maintain the correct composition of the body fluids. The tubules join up into a duct called a ureter. The urine flows down this and into the bladder and then to the outside.

VERTICAL SECTION THROUGH THE KIDNEY

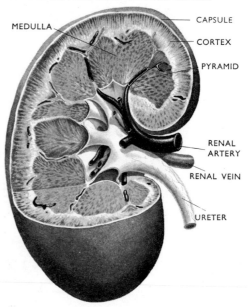

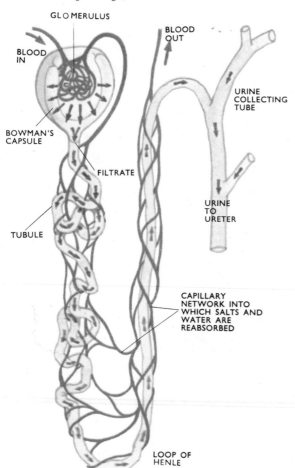

This is the basic pattern and action of the vertebrate kidney, but the problems facing different animals vary according to the conditions in which they live. This accounts for the great variation in the development of the tubules in different animals.

Freshwater fishes face a similar problem to freshwater invertebrates.

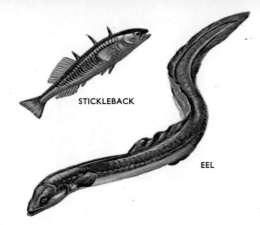

STICKLEBACK

EEL

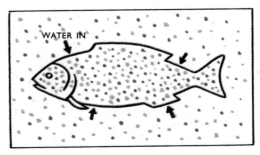

WATER IN

Their body fluids are more concentrated than the water in which they live. Thus they tend to imbibe water and lose salt. Various special modifications restrict these tendencies. Bony fishes have a covering of waterproof scales, and in many (e.g. eels) the skin produces large quantities of slime. The entry of water into the body is largely restricted therefore to the gills and lining of the mouth. The kidneys have numerous glomeruli for filtering off large quantities of water.

In bony fishes living in the sea the problem is the reverse since the blood contains less salt than the sea water. The fish must therefore retain water and remove salt. They have kidneys in which there are few glomeruli, thus reducing the amount of water lost in the filtering process. But besides this they also swallow large quantities of sea water, getting rid of the salt that they take in through special salt-releasing cells in the gills. Nitrogen-containing waste may also be excreted by the gills.

It is not known how such fishes as the Trout and Salmon cope with life

Freshwater fishes have the same problem as freshwater invertebrates. They have a waterproof covering of scales and in many (e.g. eels) the skin produces large quantities of slime, restricting the entry of water into the body largely to the gills and the mouth lining.

in both the sea and fresh water for many move from the sea into rivers to spawn. European eels go in the opposite direction to breed, leaving their rivers and streams to go on their long migration across the Atlantic Ocean to the Sargasso Sea.

Frogs have a moist skin and, when they return to water to breed, large quantities of water must pass in through it. Their kidneys have many glomeruli (the tubules are short) and measurements on the Common Frog show that they may produce about one third of an ounce of urine per day—a

Salt-water fish face the reverse problem to freshwater fish since the blood contains less salt than the sea. They swallow large quantities of sea water to obtain water, but then have to remove salt through their gills.

SALT OUT OF GILLS

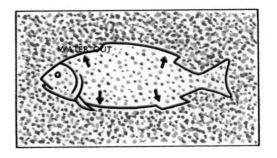

WATER OUT

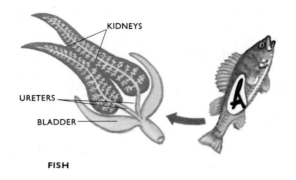

KIDNEYS

URETERS

BLADDER

FISH

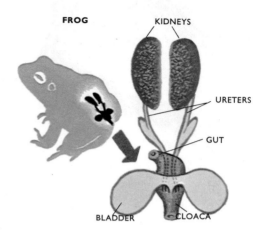

FROG

KIDNEYS

URETERS

GUT

BLADDER   CLOACA

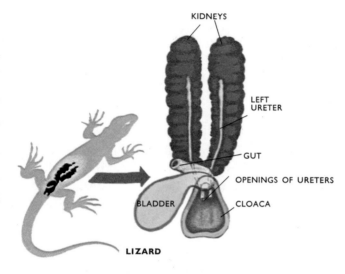

KIDNEYS

LEFT URETER

GUT

OPENINGS OF URETERS

BLADDER

CLOACA

LIZARD

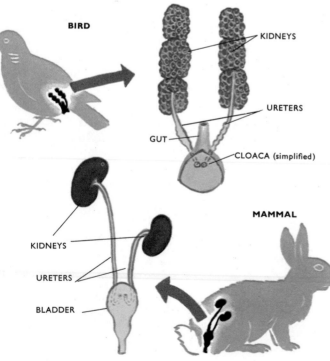

BIRD

KIDNEYS

URETERS

GUT

CLOACA (simplified)

MAMMAL

KIDNEYS

URETERS

BLADDER

third of their weight. Adult frogs excrete urea and so lose less water than their eggs and tadpoles which excrete ammonia, a more harmful substance which can remain within the body in only extreme dilutions. Frogs and toads have a bladder from which some water is reabsorbed.

Reptiles (e.g. lizards) excrete uric acid, though in most turtles urea is excreted. The capsules of the kidney tubes are small so that the amount of water filtered off is relatively small. A 'bladder' is also present (in turtles and most lizards) and, during the time that the urine is retained, much of the water is reabsorbed through its walls.

Both birds and mammals have a re-absorbing loop in the middle of the length of the kidney tubules so that a concentrated urine is produced. In birds uric acid, an almost insoluble substance, is the nitrogen-containing waste material excreted. Water loss is thus reduced to a minimum. The *cloaca* into which the gut and ureters empty is divided into chambers where much of the water in the faeces and the urine is absorbed.

Diagrams to show the positions of the excretory systems of a fish, frog, lizard, bird and mammal and their arrangement.

40

CHAPTER EIGHT

The Nervous System

IN vertebrates, as in molluscs such as the octopus and in arthropods, nervous tissue is concentrated at the anterior (front) end of the body, forming the brain. The vertebrate nervous system is characterised by this well marked *centralisation* and by the presence of large amounts of nerve tissue, by the actions of which the typical vertebrate behaviour patterns are controlled. While some parts of the brain are concerned with receiving signals from *receptor organs*, such as eyes and ears, and with sending signals to *effector organs* (muscles or glands), other parts are not directly concerned with receiving or sending signals and are not linked with any particular region of the body. These areas of the brain can over-rule the rest of the nervous system and so regulate the actions of the animal.

In other words, these regions are responsible for the "intelligence" of the animal, for its awareness of its surroundings and for the powers of learning. As one would expect, these *association centres* are more highly developed in mammals than in any other animals, and especially so in the apes and man.

The *central nervous system* (consisting of the brain and spinal cord) is hollow and situated above (dorsal to) the gut. This contrasts with the solid ventral nerve cord of the invertebrates. The vertebrate nerve cord and brain contain a liquid – the *cerebrospinal fluid* – which itself contains mineral salts and traces of protein and sugar. The fluid helps to support the nervous tissue and probably plays some part in its nutrition.

The basic vertebrate pattern is

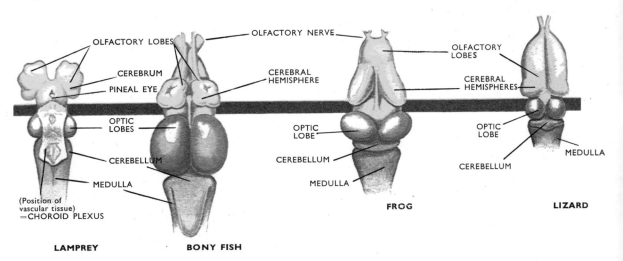

Vertebrate brains viewed from above. Brains are arranged so that the fore-brain/mid-brain junction lies on the red line. The fore-brain is coloured yellow, with red and green representing the mid- and hind-brains respectively.

shown by the lampreys and hagfishes which are the most primitive living vertebrates. The nerve fibres in these animals, however, are not covered by the fatty insulating sheath (the *myelin sheath*) which is found in all higher vertebrates. This means that nervous conduction is slow and the complex nervous connections found in higher forms are impossible in these early vertebrates.

The front part of the brain is concerned with smell – the *olfactory sense*. Nerves from the *olfactory organ* run into the thickened walls of the brain which are enlarged to form the *olfactory lobes* or *cerebral hemispheres*. Smell appears to be the only function

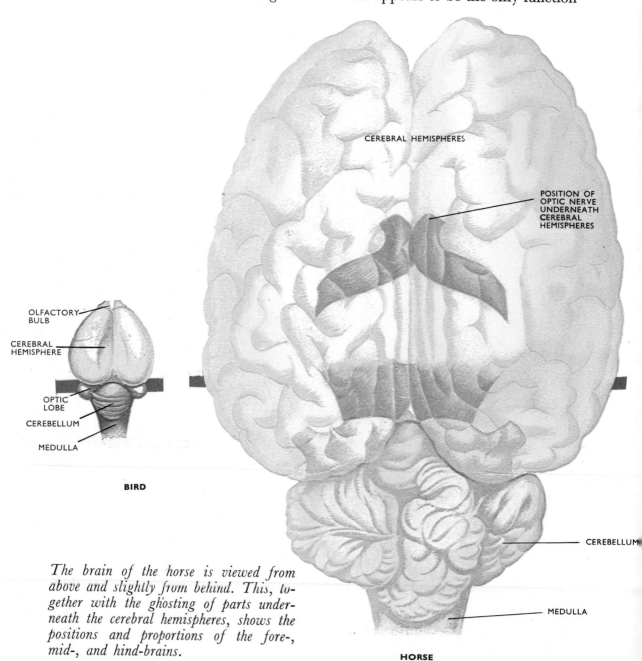

CEREBRAL HEMISPHERES

POSITION OF OPTIC NERVE UNDERNEATH CEREBRAL HEMISPHERES

OLFACTORY BULB

CEREBRAL HEMISPHERE

OPTIC LOBE

CEREBELLUM

MEDULLA

BIRD

CEREBELLUM

MEDULLA

The brain of the horse is viewed from above and slightly from behind. This, together with the ghosting of parts underneath the cerebral hemispheres, shows the positions and proportions of the fore-, mid-, and hind-brains.

HORSE

of this region in lampreys. Behind the hemispheres is the *between-brain* or *thalamus* which completes the fore-brain. The thalamus receives a few sensory nerves and carries the *pituitary body* (an important gland) on its under surface. The *pineal eye* arises on the dorsal side and reaches to the surface

The diagram shows the basic similarity of the peripheral nervous system of man and the frog.

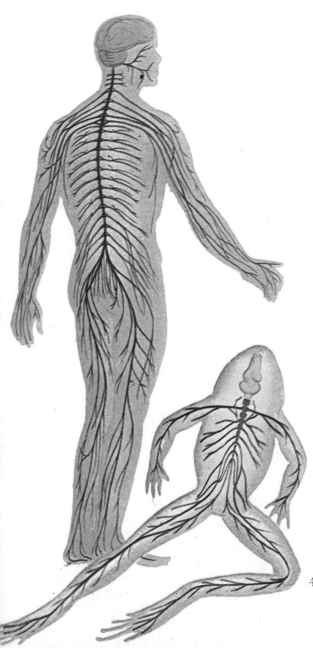

of the head. It is sensitive to light in the lamprey but much reduced in higher vertebrates.

The *mid-brain*, behind the thalamus, deals with the sense of sight. Its walls are expanded to form the *optic lobes*. Nerves pass from the mid-brain region to the motor nerves of the spinal cord and it is through these that the animal is able to act upon the signals it receives from the eyes. This system can therefore be termed an elementary association centre or centre of intelligence.

The *hind-brain* consists of the *cerebellum* and the *medulla oblongata*. The former is concerned with the regulation of balance and movement and is not well developed in lampreys which spend much of their time attached to rocks or to fish by means of the large sucker (*oral sucker*) round the mouth. The medulla oblongata passes directly into the spinal cord. It is concerned with the senses of taste and hearing and also with control of the pumping movements of the gills. The pressure sensing system of the lateral line also has its centre in the medulla. The large size of the medulla in lampreys is due to the importance of the oral sucker. They are connected by a large nerve. Taste and hearing are not well developed. The roof of the brain is well supplied with blood vessels (*choroid plexus*).

The spinal cord of the lamprey is uniformly grey in colour with the nerve cell bodies lying close to the central canal. Connections with other cells are made around the outside of this 'grey matter' in what corresponds to the 'white matter' of higher vertebrates. The roots of the *spinal nerves* do not join just outside the spinal cord as they do in other vertebrates. These spinal nerves extend as

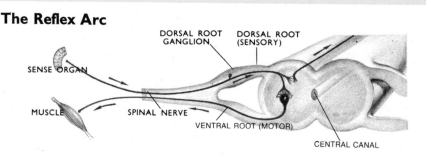

The Reflex Arc

SENSE ORGAN

DORSAL ROOT GANGLION

DORSAL ROOT (SENSORY)

MUSCLE

SPINAL NERVE

VENTRAL ROOT (MOTOR)

CENTRAL CANAL

The section of the spinal cord and nerve shows the path of nerve impulses following the reflex arc.

When a sense organ (receptor) is stimulated signals pass from it along a sensory nerve to the spinal cord. The message travels out of the spinal cord along a motor nerve to the effector organ (e.g. a muscle or gland) which acts accordingly. Such a pathway is termed a *reflex arc*. The sensory nerve fibres of a spinal nerve do not enter the spinal cord at the same place as the motor nerve fibres of the same nerve leave the spinal cord. Sensory fibres enter the dorsal part of the spinal cord while motor fibres leave the ventral part. Sensory fibres are said to have *dorsal roots* and motor fibres have *ventral roots*. The cell bodies of sensory nerves are *outside* the spinal cord, forming a swollen mass called a *dorsal root ganglion*.

the *peripheral nervous system* (the network of nerves spreading throughout the body). The peripheral system acts in much the same way as that of the invertebrates, sending and receiving impulses (signals) to and from the central nervous system.

The peripheral nervous system is very similar in all vertebrates. Paired nerves leave the spinal cord at intervals and their branches run to all parts of the body, carrying signals to and from the organs. The diagram on page 43 shows the similarity between the peripheral nervous systems of Man and a frog – members of two very different classes of vertebrates.

As the nervous systems of other vertebrates are examined it will be seen that the relative sizes of the main centres vary according to the habits of the animal and the senses on which it relies most. The association centre which was seen beginning in the mid-brain of the lamprey, develops further in the higher vertebrates until in man are found the complex patterns of learning, reasoning and memory.

CHAPTER NINE

Ageing in Animals

WHEN animals grow old, notable changes take place in their appearances. In Man, amongst other things, the skin wrinkles, the hair whitens and the step becomes uncertain. The direct causes of some of these visible features of age are known. For instance, the hair whitens simply because pigment is no longer produced. But the underlying reasons for the ageing process as a whole are not nearly so certain.

To begin with, the very definition of ageing is difficult. Of the variety of old-age symptoms, several of which can be accurately measured, no one can be taken as a standard of the overall process. For instance, is a slowing of the kidney's filtering action a more 'significant' sign of age than a weakening of muscular activity?

Measurement of any single factor produces variable results and even exceptions to a rule. Unfortunately, the long-term measurements of numerous characters for many people or animals have never been systematically kept.

One indirect method of measuring ageing is the susceptibility of the individual to non-infectious diseases. It seems a fundamental truth that most organisms, as they grow older, are less able to adapt themselves to changes and influences in their surroundings. Diseases encroach because animals are no longer able to cope with certain adverse conditions. Excessive coldness and dampness, too little food, leave an old animal more vulnerable than younger specimens. Complementary to the falling off in resistance there is also a decline in

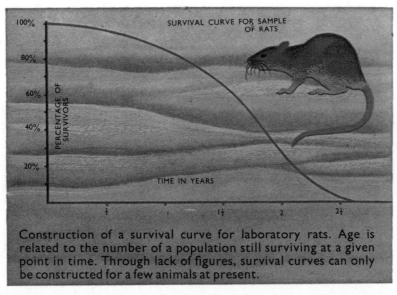

Construction of a survival curve for laboratory rats. Age is related to the number of a population still surviving at a given point in time. Through lack of figures, survival curves can only be constructed for a few animals at present.

the ability to exercise.

Here then is one approach to the process of ageing – discovering just why a body loses its resistance, strength and stamina. A direct answer is that some types of cell, at a certain age, become unable or unlikely to divide. Examples are the muscle cells and nerve cells.

Once the organs made from these cells are complete – the brain for example is composed largely of nerve cells – the cells gradually lose their ability to divide, and do not replace cells in the organ that becomes

damaged. Consequently, as losses cannot be made good, the power of the organ declines. A poor memory, for instance, is a common symptom in elderly people and far more time is usually needed for problems to be solved. Other structures known to become impaired in old age are the kidneys, lung tissues, many hormone-producing structures such as the adrenal glands, and taste buds on the tongue. All sorts of disabilities of age can be related to the death and disappearance of cells from the tissues. Associated with this disappearance is the overall decline in body weight. Muscles become emaciated and individual organs lighter.

The actual 'death' of individual cells may possibly be caused in one of two ways. They may become clogged up with insoluble wastes produced as a consequence of living processes; microscopic examination has shown muscle and nerve cells accumulate materials in this way. Or changes (*mutations*) in the cell nucleus may

ANIMAL	APPROX POTENTIAL AGES IN YEARS
RHINOCEROS	45
GORILLA	40
LION	30
SEAL	20
RABBIT	10–15
NEWT	35
TOAD	35
CROCODILE	60
SEA ANEMONE	80–100
EARTHWORM	5–10
LOBSTER	50

The smaller the animal the shorter usually the potential life span. This is well indicated in the mammals listed. The facts support the theory that death is due to irrevocable loss of cells. Of even more relevance is size of brain. Animals of relatively small stature (such as Man) having a large brain are all long-lived. Above, potential ages of some selected animals.

ELEPHANT (70–80 YEARS)

HIPPOPOTAMUS (50 YEARS)

DEER (20–30 YEARS)

ZEBRA (40 YEARS)

MOUSE (3–4 YEARS)

THE ESTABLISHED POTENTIAL AGES OF A FEW MAMMALS

The larger tortoises live well over 100 years and some may approach 200 years. Perhaps the slowness to age is due in some way to a continuous if imperceptible increase in size throughout their lives.

cause the cell to lose its ability to properly function. The chemical substance known as DNA, responsible for the construction of genes, is probably in some way affected.

Comparing Life Spans

The warm-blooded mammals and birds all age; that is, they decline in vigour and adaptability with time. Amongst the mammals there seems to be some relation between size and life span. Larger mammals as a rule live longer. Elephants are known to live to about 70 years, horses up to 40 years, cows 30 years, dogs 20 years or so, mice only about 4 years.

These are maximum ages (potential longevities); the average ages are considerably less. Of even greater significance is the relationship between life span and brain size. Large-brained species are all long-lived, despite relatively small statures. Thus Man commonly lives for 70 years or more, out-living even the elephant. Such observations are consistent with the theory that ageing is primarily due to cell destruction, particularly nerve cell destruction. The more cells initially present, the longer the life span.

Birds usually have even longer natural life spans than mammals of

Size for size birds outlive the mammals – this despite their very high metabolic rate. Of mammals, bats have unexpectedly long lives; perhaps a low metabolic rate during hibernation is significant in this instance.

EAGLE (70–80 YEARS)

SEAGULL (40 YEARS)

BAT (12–15 YEARS)

STARLING (20 YEARS)

equal size. Parrots and eagles probably can live for over a hundred years, crows, pigeons, gulls, jays all 40 years, and even small birds such as the chaffinch, when kept from natural competition, reach twenty years or so (though under natural competition their average life span is less than a year).

Collagen makes up about one third of the body's proteins. It is a highly elastic substance but with age it becomes more and more rigid, losing its former flexibility. As a result, in elderly people the skin, which contains collagen fibres as connective tissues, loses its resilience. Wrinkles and lines begin to appear. Collagen also protects arteries and fills the spaces between the cells of many vital organs. The alterations in its properties probably impair the functioning of such structures.

The changes in the properties of collagen is possibly due to the formation of crosslinks between molecules. They cannot be broken by enzymes in the body and so 'toughen' the collagen. If this is the correct answer there still remains the question why the crosslinks form.

Coming to cold-blooded amphibians and reptiles, natural life spans begin to lengthen. Perhaps the lower metabolic rate of cold-blooded creatures is an important factor. Though against this birds, animals with the highest metabolic rate of all, tend to outlive mammals of equal size.

Small frogs, toads and newts all can live for more than twenty years. Tortoises commonly live to be a century and large specimens may exceed 150 years, even approach 200 years. Some fishes, too, are known to reach colossal ages. Carp reach 50 years and sturgeons perhaps 100 years.

One possible reason for the longevity of some of the larger cold-blooded creatures is that they continually grow. Perhaps, unlike the birds and mammals, they do not have a fixed adult size. Increasing almost indefinitely in size (though the rate of growth becomes slower and slower) a creature such as the tortoise may age almost imperceptibly.

The great differences in longevity between species and even individuals of the same species rather indicate that, whether or not there is a primary cause for ageing, many other genetical and environmental factors have influence. Such factors can only be assessed after exhaustive research into the ageing of all sorts of species of animal.

Fishes

The Range of Fishes

1) Lamprey	7) Bowfin
2) Dogfish	8) Herring
3) Ray	9) Sea horse
4) Bichir	10) Angler fish
5) Gar-pike	11) Lung-fish
6) Sturgeon	12) Coelacanth

The words 'reptile' and 'bird' are precise in meaning, for they denote a member of a particular class of vertebrate animals. The word 'fish', however, although extremely useful, is not scientifically precise, for there is no class 'Fishes'. The animals usually referred to as fishes belong to several classes. All are aquatic and are constructed on a similar pattern, but there are a number of important differences between the classes.

The class Elasmobranchii contains the sharks and rays whose skeletons are made up completely of cartilage. The class Actinopterygii is by far the largest of the 'fishy' classes with more than 20,000 living species. The skeleton is usually made of true bone and the fins are membranous and supported by bony rays. The members of this class are thus often called the ray-finned fishes. They include the herring, carp, sea-horse, eel and almost all other common fishes. The third class of living fishes is the Crossopterygii. Members of this class have true bony skeletons but their fins have fleshy lobes at the base. There are only a few living species in this class – most of its members died out long ago after giving rise to the ancestors of the land vertebrates. The living lung-fishes are very specialised survivors of this class but the coelacanth seems to have remained almost unchanged for millions of years. A few extinct classes are also usually grouped with the fishes.

The lampreys and hagfishes, although very different from all the fishes mentioned so far, are frequently dealt with with the fishes. They are the survivors of a very ancient group of vertebrate animals called the Agnatha, which literally means 'without jaws', for these animals have no jaws – food is sucked into the mouth and swallowed. These animals also have no paired fins. Young lampreys show some similarities to the protochordates from which the vertebrates are believed to have arisen.

CHAPTER TEN

Feeding and Digestion

THE food of fishes falls into three main classes – small floating organisms, other fishes, and bottom-living creatures such as molluscs and starfishes. Each species of fish keeps more or less to one type of diet and the mouth and teeth are well adapted to this diet.

Fishes feeding on small floating organisms usually have their mouths at the very front of the head and make darting movements at the prey which is gulped down with the water. Teeth in these fishes are generally poorly developed.

Those fishes which feed on other fishes usually have well developed teeth – not only on the jaw bones, but on the roof of the mouth and on other bones as well. They are more or less conical and all point backwards, thus preventing the escape of the prey when it has been caught. They do not do much towards the breaking up of the food, although the sharp edges of shark teeth can cer-

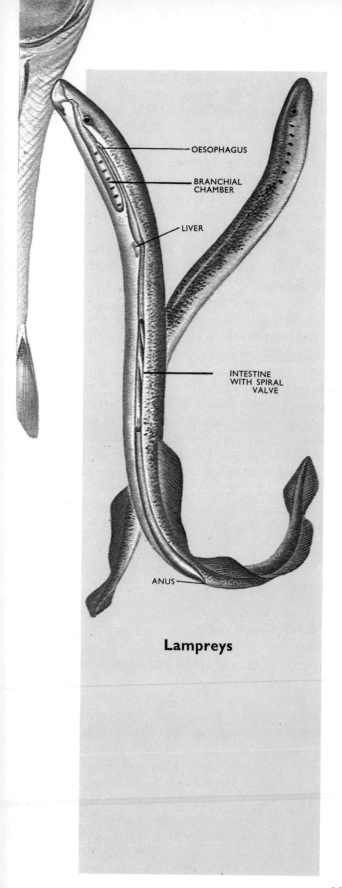

OESOPHAGUS

BRANCHIAL
CHAMBER

LIVER

INTESTINE
WITH SPIRAL
VALVE

ANUS

Lampreys

tainly cut through the flesh of their prey. The mouth is again usually at the front of the head, although this is not the case in sharks.

Bottom-feeders normally have the mouth directed to the underside of the body. Their teeth are more or less plate-like and well suited to their job of crushing molluscs.

Lampreys feed mainly on other fishes. Although they have no jaws, they have a toothed tongue with which they rasp away the flesh of their prey. The food is then sucked into the mouth. This material is easily digested and the lamprey gut is relatively simple.

The oesophagus, a narrow tube, leads from the mouth straight to the intestine; there is no stomach comparable to that of other vertebrates. The liver produces bile which is stored in the gall bladder. The bile duct from this opens into the intestine just behind its junction with the oesophagus. Patches of tissue on the intestine wall, the forerunner of part of the pancreas in higher forms, release an enzyme that is similar in action to trypsin in man. The intestine is a more or less straight tube and is not looped and coiled like that of most vertebrates. Its effective length is increased, however, by a spiral valve inside it. The food in the intestine has to follow the spiral and is thus in contact with the intestine wall for longer than it would otherwise be. Maximum absorption of food is thus ensured.

The digestive systems of sharks and of bony fishes are essentially the same as the basic vertebrate system described in an earlier chapter. The lining of the mouth and pharynx produces a mucus which moistens the

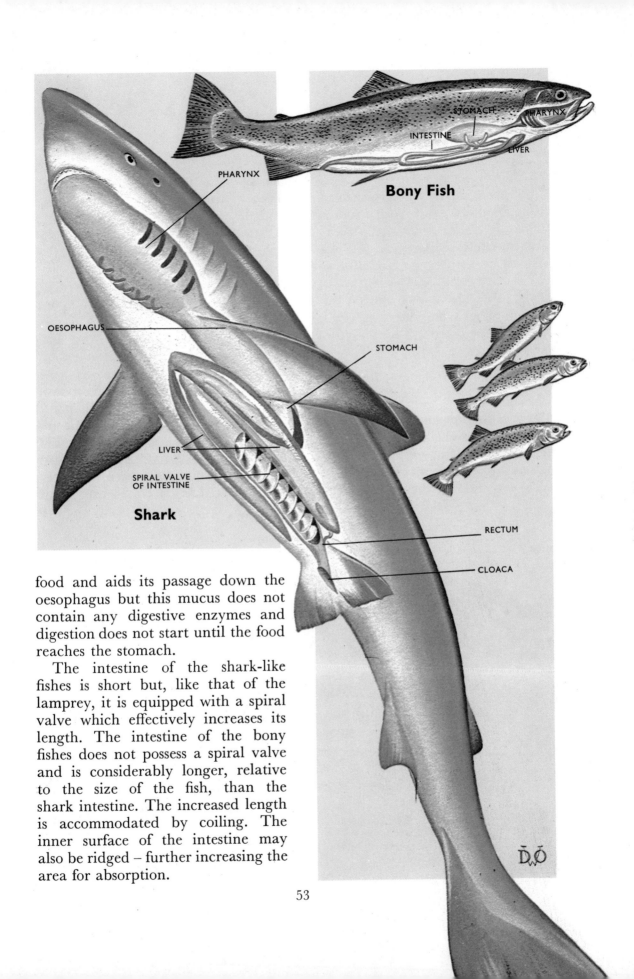

Bony Fish

PHARYNX

OESOPHAGUS

STOMACH

LIVER

SPIRAL VALVE OF INTESTINE

Shark

RECTUM

CLOACA

STOMACH

PHARYNX

INTESTINE

LIVER

food and aids its passage down the oesophagus but this mucus does not contain any digestive enzymes and digestion does not start until the food reaches the stomach.

The intestine of the shark-like fishes is short but, like that of the lamprey, it is equipped with a spiral valve which effectively increases its length. The intestine of the bony fishes does not possess a spiral valve and is considerably longer, relative to the size of the fish, than the shark intestine. The increased length is accommodated by coiling. The inner surface of the intestine may also be ridged – further increasing the area for absorption.

53

CHAPTER ELEVEN

Breathing in Fishes

MANY vertebrates live in water – the fishes, turtles, newts, whales, seals, and others – but, with rare exceptions, only the fishes are able to live completely submerged. All the others must surface periodically to breathe. Oxygen dissolves in water and the fishes are able to extract this dissolved oxygen and use it for respiration. They extract it by means of their gills.

Gills

The gills are essentially very thin plates of tissue suspended in channels connecting the throat region (pharynx) of the fish with the outside. The outer openings of these channels are the gill slits. In the cartilaginous fishes – the sharks, rays, and dog-fishes – the slits are visible on the outside of the body but in the bony fishes they are covered by the operculum which is open only on the hind edge.

If you watch a fish in an aquarium, you will see that it continually opens and shuts its mouth. This is its breathing movement. As the fish opens its mouth and lowers the floor of the pharynx, water flows into the mouth. The fish then shuts its mouth and raises the floor of the pharynx. The water is then forced out of the gill slits. The gills are well supplied with blood which has just been round the body. This blood therefore contains very little oxygen – much less

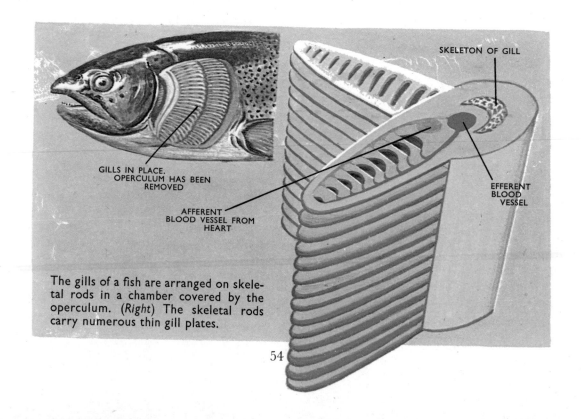

GILLS IN PLACE. OPERCULUM HAS BEEN REMOVED

SKELETON OF GILL

AFFERENT BLOOD VESSEL FROM HEART

EFFERENT BLOOD VESSEL

The gills of a fish are arranged on skeletal rods in a chamber covered by the operculum. (*Right*) The skeletal rods carry numerous thin gill plates.

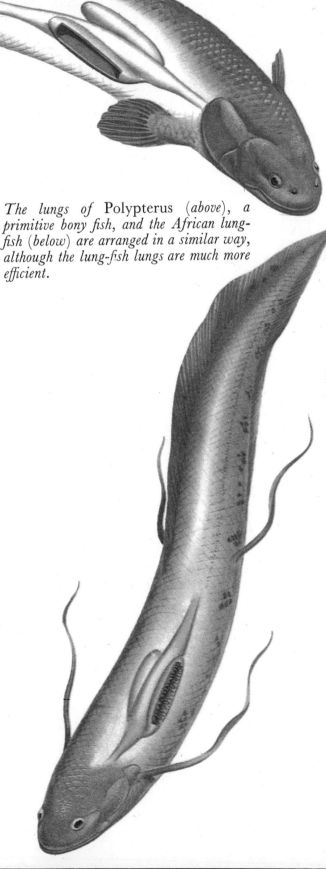

than the water flowing over the gills contains. Oxygen therefore passes from the water, through the very thin gill walls, and into the blood. It is then carried round the body and distributed to the tissues. The fish is able to close its gill slits while it takes water in through the mouth and open them again when the mouth closes. The fish can also close up the entrance to the food canal so that water does not go straight down into the stomach.

Lampreys have a slightly different arrangement of the gills. There are seven circular openings on each side of the body (there are only five pairs of gills in other fishes) and each opening leads to a pouch containing gills. The pouches do not open into the pharynx, however. The lamprey pumps water in and out of the pouch through the one opening. This is associated with the method of feeding. With its mouth firmly attached to its prey, the lamprey could not use it for breathing.

Lungs

Although gills are the main breathing organs of fishes, many of them can augment their oxygen supply by gulping air. The throat region is well supplied with blood, and oxygen can pass from the water and into the bloodstream. Fishes often gulp air if the water is polluted and therefore short of oxygen.

The lungs of Polypterus *(above), a primitive bony fish, and the African lung-fish (below) are arranged in a similar way, although the lung-fish lungs are much more efficient.*

55

This air-gulping is taken a stage further in some fishes – they actually have lungs. These are pouches growing out from the back end of the pharynx just as the lungs of land animals do. The lungs of the bichir – an African river fish – are not very efficient and it relies mainly on its gills. This fish cannot live out of water. The internal surface of the lung is smooth and there is not a large surface for oxygen absorption. The African lung-fish, on the other hand, will die if it cannot gulp air and it can survive out of water, as long as it does not completely dry up. Its lungs have complicated linings with a large area for oxygen absorption.

The bichir is a survivor from the ancient group which gave rise to the modern ray-finned fishes. The African lung-fish (together with related forms in South America and Australia) is a survivor of the groups which long ago gave rise to the land vertebrates. The further development of the lung is obvious in the latter case but what happened to it when the modern ray-finned fishes arose from bichir-like ancestors?

The Air Bladder

Above the food canal (that is to say *dorsal* in position) there is often found a hollow balloon-like structure called the *swim-bladder*. The swim-bladder acts like the ballast tanks of a submarine. By filling with gas it lowers the specific gravity of the fish so that the fish rises in the water. By expelling the gas, the specific gravity of the fish is increased and the fish sinks. In the front of the bladder is a red portion of tissue very richly supplied with blood vessels called, appropriately, the *red body*. It is from these blood vessels that gas is obtained when inflation of the bladder is necessary.

At first inspection the swim-bladder does not appear to be in any way related to a lung. But some ray-finned fish still have the bladder connected to the pharnyx by a tube. The positions of both the tube and the bladder have moved from the original ventral situation to a dorsal position. This has happened to the lungs of the lungfishes also. The dorsal position of the lung gives far greater stability to the fish. A ventral lung would tend to make the fish top-heavy and cause it to roll over.

Almost certainly, the swim-bladder of the ray-finned fish has evolved from the primitive lung. The majority of ray-finned fish appear to have left fresh-water at some stage and invaded the sea. Here there was no danger of drought and the water was not stagnant. The conversion of the lung to a built-in ballast tank was of great value. The flesh and bone of a fish is denser than the surrounding water and causes the fish to sink. But the air bladder when inflated lowers the overall density and the fish can keep up without actually swimming. This advantage is one of the reasons why the ray-finned fishes are more varied and numerous than the other fishes – the sharks and their allies.

Some bottom-dwelling ray-finned fishes show no sign of a swim-bladder. This is not surprising as it is not needed in such surroundings. Usually however swim-bladders are present when they are very young. Two American fishes, the bowfin and the gar-pike, have returned to fresh-water. The swim-bladder of these fishes is once more used for breathing air.

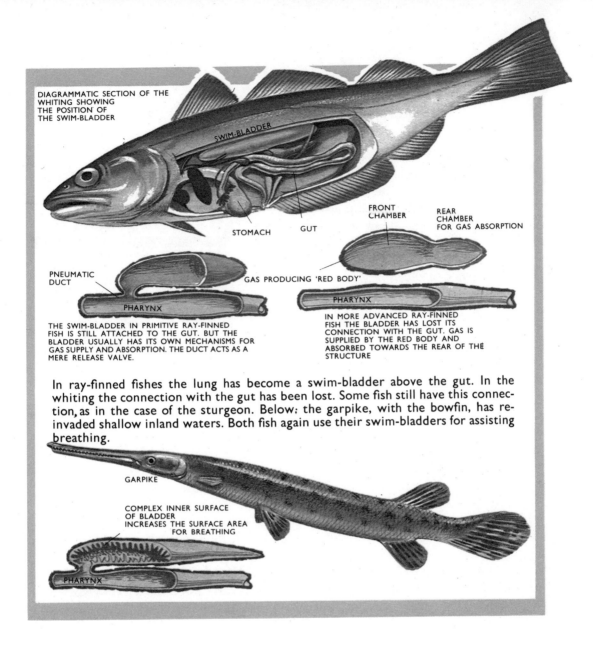

DIAGRAMMATIC SECTION OF THE
WHITING SHOWING
THE POSITION OF
THE SWIM-BLADDER

SWIM-BLADDER

STOMACH

GUT

FRONT
CHAMBER

REAR
CHAMBER
FOR GAS ABSORPTION

PNEUMATIC
DUCT

GAS PRODUCING 'RED BODY'

PHARYNX

PHARYNX

THE SWIM-BLADDER IN PRIMITIVE RAY-FINNED
FISH IS STILL ATTACHED TO THE GUT. BUT THE
BLADDER USUALLY HAS ITS OWN MECHANISMS FOR
GAS SUPPLY AND ABSORPTION. THE DUCT ACTS AS A
MERE RELEASE VALVE.

IN MORE ADVANCED RAY-FINNED
FISH THE BLADDER HAS LOST ITS
CONNECTION WITH THE GUT. GAS IS
SUPPLIED BY THE RED BODY AND
ABSORBED TOWARDS THE REAR OF THE
STRUCTURE

In ray-finned fishes the lung has become a swim-bladder above the gut. In the
whiting the connection with the gut has been lost. Some fish still have this connection, as in the case of the sturgeon. Below; the garpike, with the bowfin, has re-
invaded shallow inland waters. Both fish again use their swim-bladders for assisting
breathing.

GARPIKE

COMPLEX INNER SURFACE
OF BLADDER
INCREASES THE SURFACE AREA
FOR BREATHING

PHARYNX

CHAPTER TWELVE

The Nervous System

THE simplest vertebrate brain – that of the lamprey – has been described in an earlier chapter. The brains of the typical fishes show a number of advances on this basic pattern – mainly concerned with their more active way of life.

The cerebral hemispheres of fishes are still concerned almost entirely with the sense of smell. The floor of this region is developed but the roof remains thin and has no nerves. The floor receives nerves from the olfactory organs and in the sharks, which rely on smell for hunting their food, the cerebral hemispheres are large. In the salmon (and most other bony fishes), which relies on sight for getting its food, the cerebral hemispheres are dwarfed by the large optic lobes. The mid-brain receives nerves from organs and regions other than the eyes and is able to 'add up' the signals received and act accordingly. There is therefore a more highly organised association centre here. Fish are, on the whole, active animals and the cerebellum is enlarged in order that it can efficiently control the movement and balance of the animal. The medulla is not generally a significant region but, in fish like the carp which find food by taste, the *gustatory* (taste) region is enlarged to very nearly the size of the optic lobes.

The Special Senses

The mastery that fishes have established over other water-dwelling creatures is largely due to the possession of highly developed sense

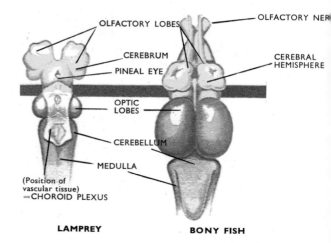

OLFACTORY LOBES
OLFACTORY NER
CEREBRUM
CEREBRAL HEMISPHERE
PINEAL EYE
OPTIC LOBES
CEREBELLUM
MEDULLA
(Position of vascular tissue)
=CHOROID PLEXUS

LAMPREY   BONY FISH

The brains are viewed from above and arranged so that the fore-brain/mid-brain junction lies on the red line.

organs, specially suited for life in the water.

Touch

Our knowledge of touch receptors and those for pain, heat, and cold detection in fishes is scanty. These senses are not so well developed in shark-like fishes as in bony fishes, for the former have a tough skin in which are embedded numerous horny, tooth-like scales or denticles.

There are undoubtedly receptors for touch and pain though the way in which they work has not been analysed.

In bony fishes the sense of touch is very well developed. Many species have tentacles or filaments, particularly near the mouth. These are very sensitive. Catfish, mullets, barbels, cod, haddock and sturgeons have filaments of this type. In others (e.g. the Gurnard) the pectoral ('shoulder') fins are modified. The Gurnard also has receptors on these fins that are sensitive to chemicals.

Taste and Smell

Senses for the detection of chemicals are well developed in fishes. Sharks and bony fishes have a pair of nostrils not unlike those of higher animals but, except in lung fishes, they do not open internally into the mouth cavity though they may have in and out channels. They are placed in front of the mouth or on the upper side of head.

Fishes can detect minute traces of chemicals in the water and, in this way, may locate both food and enemies. In hunting their prey some fishes rely more on scent than sight, and accordingly the olfactory (smell) parts of the brain are better developed.

As in higher animals, the nose is used to locate objects at a distance—the smell receptors are called *distance receptors*. Similarly, fishes have taste receptors that sample chemicals close to them. But whereas we have taste receptors only on our tongue and on certain parts of the wall of the mouth, bony fishes, at any rate, have them on the outside of the body too. Some species have them on the tail: the Whiting and the Gurnard have them on their pectoral fins. This makes an interesting comparison with insects that have taste receptors on their feet.

Experiments with some fishes (e.g. Dogfish) show that they can distinguish the four taste qualities—salt, sweet, sour (acid) and bitter.

Sight

The structure of the eyes in fishes is similar to that of other vertebrates—in fact very like our own. They can be moved up and down and from left

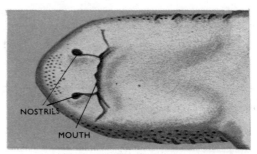

The position of the nostrils in a dogfish.

to right by an arrangement of muscles like that of other vertebrates. However, whilst our own eye is focused by altering the shape of the lens, in fishes the lens is moved backwards and forwards; that is, towards or away from the retina. In some fishes (e.g. Trout) the iris has little or no adjustment, but in others (e.g. Angler fish) it is highly mobile.

The colours of bony fishes are brilliant and varied. It is not surprising, therefore, that colour vision is well developed in many of them, though it does not follow that a colour is bright and striking to another fish just because it appears bright to us. Experiments show, however, that many fishes (e.g. Goldfish) detect the difference between two different colours of the same brightness. A wide range of colour patterns is used in

A diagram of a section through the eye of a bony fish.

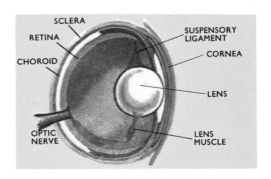

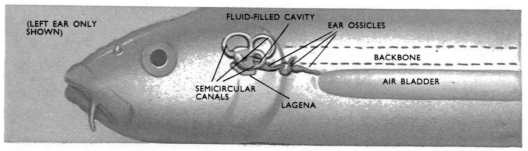

A diagram showing the relationship of the inner ear, ear ossicles and air bladder in a carp-like fish.

courtship display and the males are often brightly coloured whereas the females are dull and drab coloured. Examples of this occur in the Cuckoo wrasse and the Stickleback. Male Sticklebacks will certainly attack red-coloured models that are placed near them in the water—exactly the natural reaction that they have against other males in order to preserve their territory.

Hearing and Balance

The ears of fishes are similar to the inner part of our own. The *cochlea* or *lagena* is not coiled and lacks the complicated structures (e.g. *basilar membrane*) found in the human ear. Yet experiments show that this is the hearing organ.

There is no eardrum and no ear passage in communication with the outer world. Sound waves are received, in most cases, by the lagena directly through the fish's body (having travelled through the water). Many fishes produce sounds, the detection of which is probably important at times of spawning.

Besides the lagena there are two other chambers nearby, the *sacculus* and *utriculus*, and three *semi-circular canals* arranged in three planes and approximately at right angles to each other (as in the human ear).

Each chamber contains a chalky ear-stone or *otolith*—these press down on nerve endings and inform the fish what its position is in relation to the direction in which gravity acts.

In some fishes there is a special chain of bones—the *Weberian ossicles*—attached to the backbone and linking the ear with the air bladder. This arrangement is present in carps and cat-fishes, for example. In World War II, microphones were placed in submerged hollow containers, for the latter act as amplifiers in a liquid, and so submarines could be detected more easily. Undoubtedly the air-bladders amplify the vibrations received by the fish and these amplified vibrations are then 'relayed' to the lagena along the chain of ossicles. It is interesting that carps and catfishes have excellent hearing whereas some bony fishes (lacking the above amplifying devices) are almost deaf.

The Lateral Line System

This remarkable system of sense organs is found only in fishes and in the young (tadpole) stages of frogs and other amphibians. It is better developed in bony fishes than in shark-like fishes. Along the sides of both sharks and bony fishes a line from the back of the head to the tail can clearly be seen. This is the *lateral line*.

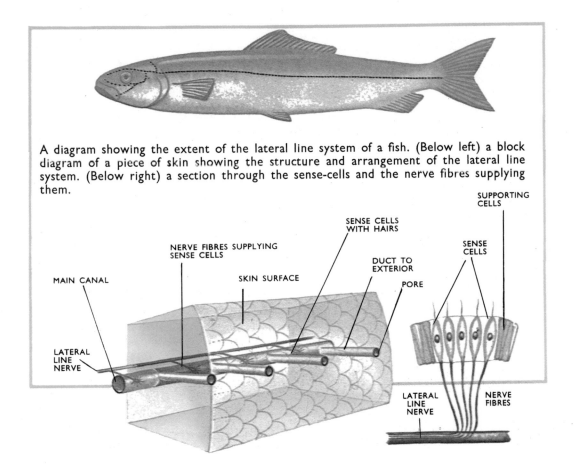

A diagram showing the extent of the lateral line system of a fish. (Below left) a block diagram of a piece of skin showing the structure and arrangement of the lateral line system. (Below right) a section through the sense-cells and the nerve fibres supplying them.

A pattern of similar lines can be seen on the head. They consist of distinct groups of sensory cells arranged in long rows and supplied with nerve endings.

The cells are protected either in an open groove running just beneath the surface of the skin or in a tube which opens to the exterior (through the scales in bony fishes, between them in sharks) at intervals by a series of pores.

Each cell has a hair-like process projecting into the water in the groove or tube. Movements and vibrations in the water round the fish move the hairs and the disturbance of the sense cell results in signals passing along nerve fibres to the brain.

The lines on the head are particularly well developed in the herring and other plankton-feeding fish. The system may play an important part in the detection of food. A certain deep-water fish has lateral line organs on stalks projecting from the sides of the body. Food is scarce in the abyssal regions of the sea: is it possible that this extraordinary development of the lateral line system helps the fish to detect prey? Alternatively, of course, it would be equally valuable in detecting disturbances of the water due to enemies.

CHAPTER THIRTEEN

Reproduction in Fishes

A short visit to the quayside to watch the fishing vessels release their catches is sufficient to impress on one's mind that there are many millions of fishes in the sea. Large numbers also inhabit lakes and rivers. Yet this vast number of individuals is but a small percentage of the potential population. If all the eggs were to survive, the sea would literally be jam-packed with fishes. A female cod may contain as many as nine million eggs, halibut more than two million, herring thirty to fifty thousand. Of course, the sea could not support such a population. Many of the eggs are eaten by fishes, often by fishes of the same species, and many are not even fertilized. The chances of an egg or of a young fish surviving are very low so that the production of so many eggs is necessary for the numbers to be maintained.

Many shark-like fishes lay each of their eggs in a horny 'Mermaid's Purse'.

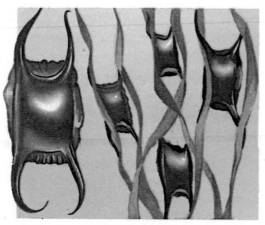

Not all fishes produce as many eggs as those quoted above. As a general rule, the numbers depend on the degree of care that the eggs and young receive from the parent fishes. Female sticklebacks lay from fifty to a hundred eggs only, in an elaborate nest usually constructed of seaweed in marine species, or algal threads and water weeds in freshwater species. The nest is built by the male and he zealously guards it and its immediate surroundings (the *territory*) from intruders. Even when the eggs hatch he guards the young just as carefully until they are able to fend for themselves.

The reproductive habits of fishes vary enormously. Many, such as herring and mackerel, assemble in vast shoals prior to spawning, whilst others (e.g. salmon) form pairs. The act of pairing may be preceded by an elaborate courtship display, prior to which the male often becomes brilliantly coloured. A female salmon lays her eggs in a hollow which she has 'cut' with her tail in the gravel beds. The male sheds his sperms over the eggs after they have been laid. Some fishes perform extensive spawning migrations. Salmon return to freshwater from the sea while European and North American eels make their journeys in the reverse direction, travelling from freshwater lakes and rivers across the Atlantic to the Sargasso sea.

A remarkable association exists between the males and females of certain deep-sea fishes (e.g. Angler-fishes).

The males are tiny by comparison with the females and live permanently attached to them by their jaws. Their blood-systems are continuous so that the males are nourished by the females. The dwarf male provides sperm, however, with which the eggs of the female are fertilized. In sharks (and a few bony fishes) fertilization is internal, the sperms being guided into the female by a pair of claspers – modifications of the paired pelvic fins. Many sharks (e.g. dogfish) and most rays and skates, produce large horny egg cases – so called 'Mermaid's purses' – each of which contains a large yolky egg. The purses are laid in the water and become attached to seaweeds by means of their long coiled filaments. The embryos develop within them and are nourished by the rich supply of yolk. Many shark-like fishes bear their young alive, however (so do a few bony fishes, for example, guppies, surf fishes and live-bearers). The Spur dog carries as many as eleven young (four on average) and female Tope have been found with over thirty inside them. In the Smooth hound (*Mustelus mustelus*) the yolk sacs of the young are richly supplied with blood vessels. Finger-like projections from the wall of part of the reproductive system (*oviduct*) fit closely into pits in the yolk sacs. Such an arrangement is similar to that found in mammals, where the womb lining grows to form a highly vascular *placenta* through which the developing young are nourished. Somewhat similar arrangements are also found in a few bony fishes.

Many fish congregate in shoals for the purpose of spawning; (insets) diagrams showing several stages in the development of a pilchard.

A pair of brown trout spawning. The female, in foreground, 'cuts' a hollow in the gravel into which the eggs are laid, and the male sheds his sperms over them.

The eggs of the salmon are heavy and sticky and become attached to stones. Those of the turbot and shad are also heavy and sink to the bottom, where they may drift and roll about in the currents. Herring also lay eggs that sink, but most other commercially important fish, for example cod, pilchards, mackerel and plaice, lay floating eggs. These contain droplets of oil which make them buoyant.

Among those fishes that do look after the eggs and young, one or both parents may be involved. In lumpsuckers, sticklebacks and miller's thumbs (bullheads) it is usually the male that stands guard. The male stickleback aerates the eggs by waving its pectoral fins to produce a continual current of water. In the African lake fish (*Tilapia*) the female usually incubates and guards the eggs in her mouth. For a time after the young have hatched they are taken back into her mouth periodically, especially at the approach of danger. They are protected in this way for almost a week. In related species the male alone, or male and female in turn take the eggs and young into their mouths.

Male seahorses have a special brood pouch under the abdomen. The eggs develop in this pouch. Most of the

The reproductive system in most bony fishes consists, in the male, of a pair of *testes* (the soft roes) which open into the lower part of the channels carrying urine from the kidneys. In the female the *ovaries* (hard roes) are usually long paired structures from which oviducts carry the eggs into a chamber at the end of the urinary ducts. In some (e.g. trout) the ovaries release their eggs into the body cavity. They find their way out of this down a pair of funnels to the outside.

Paradise fishes and Gouramis build a curious nest of bubbles. They take bubbles of air into their mouths and expel them at the surface where they form a raft several inches across. The eggs are laid in this raft and develop there.

The bitterling is a fish that has an extraordinary association with certain freshwater molluscs – the mussel, *Unio*, and the swan mussel, *Anodonta*. The female bitterling has a long egg tube, the *ovipositor*, which she inserts into the inhalent siphon of the mollusc. The eggs are carried into the mollusc by the ingoing water current and they lodge in the gill cavity. The sperms of the highly coloured male bitterling also enter the mollusc by this route and fertilization of the fish eggs takes place inside the mollusc. The fish eggs develop there, well protected from enemies and supplied with a continuous current of fresh oxygen-containing water. The young bitterlings leave the mussel through the exhalent siphon soon after hatching from the eggs.

The young of an African lakefish, Tilapia, *swim into the parent's mouth where they are protected.*

The Life History of the Common Frog

(*See page 75*)

66

Amphibians

The Range of Amphibian Forms

1) *Ichthyostega (extinct)*
2) *Eryops (extinct)*
3) *Larval amphibians (tadpoles)*
4) *Mud puppy*
5) *Newt*
6) *Salamander*
7) *Ambystoma*
8) *Common toad*
9) *Surinam toad*
10) *Tree frog*
11) *Common frog*
12) *An Apodan*

INTRODUCTION

The amphibians arose more than 300 million years ago from a group of lunged fishes. At that time the climate in many parts of the world was very dry and rivers and streams were drying up. The lunged fishes were probably able to crawl up out of the drying pools and move around on their fleshy fins in search of new water. Gradually they became more and more used to being out of water and their fins gradually evolved into the typical five-fingered limbs of the land vertebrates.

The bodies of these early amphibians were still very fish-like and they were clumsy creatures with heavy scales and bones. But, although these animals were able to live on land, they had to return to water to breed, for their young stages were aquatic like their fishy ancestors.

Modern amphibians are very unlike their primitive ancestors. There has been a great reduction of bone and the skin is soft and moist, usually without scales. They are very specialised descendants of the early amphibians and they are a very successful group. Nevertheless, with few exceptions, they still have to return to the water to breed and their moist skins dictate that they must be confined to damp surroundings.

Living amphibians belong to one of three groups: the Anura – frogs and toads; the Caudata – newts and salamanders; and the Apoda – limbless burrowing animals which superficially resemble large earthworms and which are found only in tropical regions. Members of the Anura are divided into frogs and toads. The main scientific difference between the two groups is in the structure of the shoulder girdle but this feature is generally ignored when common names are given. Rough skinned anurans tend to be called toads and smooth skinned ones are generally called frogs, regardless of their true grouping. Nevertheless, the basic biology of the two groups is very similar.

CHAPTER FOURTEEN

Feeding and Digestion

ADULT amphibians are carnivorous, feeding on slugs, worms, insects, and other arthropods. Young newts are also carnivorous but the young stages of frogs and toads are vegetarians, rasping away at the water plants with their tiny teeth.

Newts and salamanders detect their prey by both sight and smell. The floor of the mouth can be moved forward as the animal snaps at its prey. Tiny teeth on the jaws and on the roof of the mouth prevent the escape of the prey which is gradually swallowed whole.

Frogs and toads detect their food only by sight – movement is the main stimulus, and these animals rarely eat dead food. The tongue in the anurans is fixed at the front end while the hind end lies free. It is the main food-catching organ. When an insect or some other unfortunate creature comes within range, the tongue is flicked out at high speed and its sticky end collects the prey and returns it to the mouth. A full-grown toad may have a tongue three quarters of an inch long. The jaws may or may not be equipped with teeth which, as in the newts, prevent the escape of the prey as it is being swallowed. The eyeballs can be withdrawn into their orbits and their lower sides bulge into the mouth where they help to squash the food and pass it down the oesophagus.

The food canal of the frog is shown in Chapter 4. It is a very simple system in all amphibians. No digestion occurs in the mouth but mucous glands in the pharynx help to lubricate the food on its way. The stomach is a simple sac and the intestine is relatively short in the adult. It is of interest that the food canal of the vegetarian tadpole is relatively longer than that of the carnivorous adult. This is associated with the fact that plant material is more difficult to digest and assimilate.

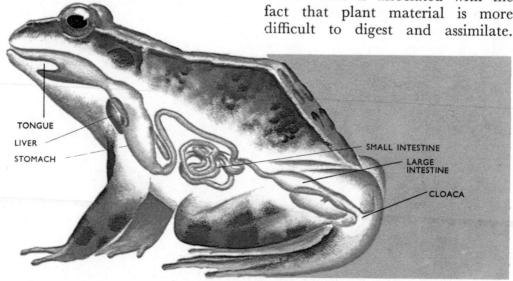

TONGUE
LIVER
STOMACH
SMALL INTESTINE
LARGE INTESTINE
CLOACA

CHAPTER FIFTEEN

Breathing in Amphibians

ALTHOUGH the amphibians normally have lungs, these are not very efficient breathing organs. They are rather small and their internal surfaces are not very complicated. There is thus only a small surface for the absorption of oxygen. The lining of the mouth and throat region is very well supplied with blood vessels and this region plays an important part in breathing.

The ribs of amphibians are very poorly developed and the animals cannot increase the size of the chest cavity. They pump air into the lungs whereas mammals suck it in. The amphibian mouth usually stays shut. When the animal breathes in the nostrils are open and the floor of the throat is lowered by a special structure called the *hyoid apparatus*. Air is thus drawn into the mouth and throat. The nostrils are then closed and the floor of the throat is brought up, forcing air into the lungs. Dropping of the floor again will draw the air back from the lungs into the mouth. This may happen several times before the air is expelled through the nostrils. Thus, while obtaining a large percentage of oxygen from the inspired air and removing large amounts of carbon dioxide, the quantity of water that is lost as vapour is reduced to a minimum.

An alternative breathing method is to keep the nostrils open and merely to draw air into the mouth cavity and force it out again. This is especially important to those amphibians with reduced lungs.

The skin is also an important site of breathing. It is very thin and moist and oxygen can pass through very easily and into the blood vessels just below the surface. A number of salamanders and anurans live permanently in water and some of them have no lungs. They obtain all their oxygen through the skin.

Young amphibians – the tadpoles – live in water and breathe by means of gills. When the tadpoles first hatch from the eggs, the gills are feathery outgrowths from the side of the body. These external gills remain throughout the larval life in the newts and salamanders but in the anurans they are replaced after a few days by internal gills very similar to those of fishes.

The frog absorbs much oxygen through the skin and mouth, and the surface area of its lungs is small.

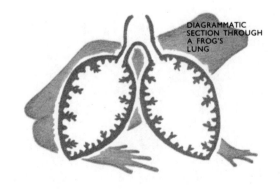

DIAGRAMMATIC SECTION THROUGH A FROG'S LUNG

CHAPTER SIXTEEN

The Nervous System

THE amphibian brain does not differ widely from the typical fish brain except that the cerebral hemispheres are 'roofed over' with nervous tissue. The sense of smell is still the main function of this region although a number of nerves from other sensory systems (e.g. sight) enter the hind part of the hemispheres. There are also some connections between the hemispheres and the motor system of the spinal cord, thus it can be seen that the fore-brain is growing in importance. The mid-brain, however, is still the most important region in the amphibians. Apart from the sense of sight, it deals with nerve signals from most other regions of the body and sends signals to other parts of

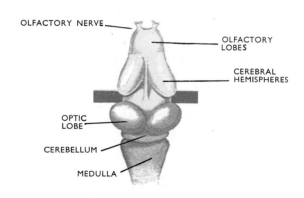

FROG BRAIN

The brain is viewed from above and arranged so that the fore-brain/mid-brain junction lies on the red line.

the brain and the spinal cord. The behaviour of an amphibian is thus dominated by the centres of the mid-brain.

CHAPTER SEVENTEEN

Amphibious Life Stories

MOST adult amphibians are able to live on land but few species have been able to move far from water. The majority of living amphibians, although highly specialised in other ways, still retain a fish-like aquatic larval stage – the tadpole. There are a number of variations on the typical life history shown by the frog, culminating in the live birth of small adult forms – the tadpole stage is passed within the mother's body. There are parallel sequences in the variation in newts and salamanders on the one hand and frogs and toads on the other.

Caudata (= Urodela)

These are the newts and salamanders – the tailed amphibians. They are often brightly coloured and vary in length from a few inches to more than five feet. Most species however are less than a foot long. The eggs are fertilized within the body of the female and before pairing there is usually an elaborate courtship display by the male.

Newts of the genus *Triturus*, found in Europe and America, as a rule exhibit the typical life history. After winter hibernation, the adults – the

The female smooth newt protects her eggs by folding the leaves on which they are laid. The young newts resemble the adult except for the gills and broad tail fin.

males in gay mating colours – enter the water and courtship begins. The male makes use of his coloration and his tail crest and after a while deposits a 'packet' of sperms. This is picked up by the female in her *cloaca* (the opening of the reproductive and excretory systems) and stored until the eggs are ripe. The eggs are laid singly or in small groups. They are covered with a sticky fluid that quickly swells upon contact with water and serves to attach the eggs to leaves. The female normally covers the eggs by folding the leaves over.

Tadpoles hatch in about two weeks and begin to feed on animal and plant food. At first they are limbless and have external feathery gills and a broad tail fin. As development goes on, legs appear and the tadpole begins to resemble a small adult. Lungs gradually develop and, in the summer, the gills disappear. So, too, does the tail fin. The newt has now *metamorphosed* (changed) into the adult stage. The young adult leaves the water and may not return for several years – until it is sexually mature. Adult newts live in damp places, feeding on slugs, worms and insects.

The tailed amphibians show many variations on this life history. The European Spotted Salamander is *viviparous* (i.e. it gives birth to active young). Pairing takes place on land and the eggs develop within the female. The tadpoles are born when the female enters the water. The Black Salamander of the Alpine regions has

The Midwife Toad lays a string of eggs which are then wrapped round the legs of the male until they are ready to hatch.

The Mudpuppy retains its larval characters throughout life. It lives in water and lays eggs from which young individuals emerge.

The Red-cheeked Salamander of N. America lives on land. The eggs hatch directly into miniature adults.

carried the process a stage further. The adults do not return to the water at all. The eggs develop, pass through the tadpole stage and change into tiny adults before leaving the mother's body. The free-living larval stage is thus suppressed. A number of salamanders lay their eggs in damp soil, under stones and similar objects. The tadpole stage is passed within the eggs and miniature adults emerge. The American Worm Salamander is an example. These last examples show how salamanders have become completely terrestrial, but some species have gone the other way and are completely aquatic.

The aquatic forms often retain larval characters, such as external gills, even in the adult stage. *Necturus*, the mud-puppy, retains the external gills, and has only tiny lungs. In other species, the limbs are not fully developed. The *axolotls* of Mexico may never acquire the typical adult characters at all: they can reach sexual maturity and breed without first metamorphosing.

Anura

These animals – the frogs and toads are very specialised and successful and are found all over the world. There are tree-living, burrowing and completely aquatic species, as well as the more typical forms. Pairing normally takes place in the water and the eggs are usually fertilized immediately after spawning. The life history of most species follows, in general, that of the common frog. Those species that lay their eggs in damp soil, spend the larval period within the egg and hatch as tiny frogs. A few species give birth to active young. There are interesting

The Life History of the Common Frog

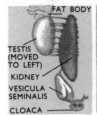
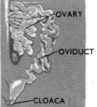

FAT BODY

TESTIS (MOVED TO LEFT)

KIDNEY

VESICULA SEMINALIS

CLOACA

OVARY

OVIDUCT

CLOACA

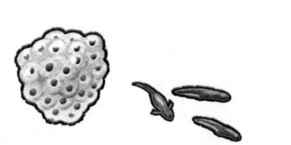

A diagram of the sexual organs of a male frog (left) and a female (right). Only half of each are shown.

Adult frogs spend the cold winter months in a state of inactivity – hidden under logs and stones, or buried in mud. They awaken in early spring and return to the water. As a rule, the males return first and, by their croaking, attract the females. Pairing takes place in the water without any courtship display. As the female discharges her eggs the male releases sperm over them and fertilization follows. The eggs are covered with jelly which quickly swells on contact with the water. It keeps the eggs together and protects them.

After fertilization, each egg-cell begins to divide and, within a few days, the black sphere elongates and develops a head and tail. The tadpole hatches in about ten days and attaches itself to a plant by means of a sticky gland. The mouth is not yet fully formed and the young tadpole exists on the yolk material from the egg. About three days after hatching, the mouth opens and the tadpole then begins to feed on algae. By this time three pairs of delicate external gills have developed.

During the next few weeks the tadpole grows rapidly and important changes take place both internally and externally. Internal gills are formed. These are respiratory openings connecting the mouth and the outside. A fold of skin (*the operculum*) covers them and opens at a single point (*the spiracle*) on the left hand side. The external gills disappear, and, apart from its large head the tadpole is like a fish. However, the legs soon begin to develop. The hind ones appear first because the front limbs are covered by the operculum. The left front limb appears through the spiracle, followed later by the right leg which breaks through the operculum. Lungs have formed by now and the tadpole begins to breathe air at the surface. It feeds on animal material now, insect larvae for example – and the mouth enlarges.

As the legs grow, the tail shortens and the typical frog shape becomes obvious. The frog has now *metamorphosed* or changed into the adult form. It leaves the water and lives in damp vegetation feeding on insects, slugs and worms. The whole process from egg to metamorphosis takes about three months but the small frog requires another three or four years to become mature and able to breed.

examples of parental care among the toads. The Midwife Toad, found in Southern Europe, pairs on land. The eggs, laid in 'strings', are then wrapped around the legs of the *male* toad. For two or three weeks the tadpoles develop within the eggs, and then the male enters the water and sheds the eggs. The tadpoles quickly hatch and develop normally. The Surinam Toad of South America is completely aquatic but the tadpoles are not free-swimming. As the eggs are laid they are passed on to the back of the female where they sink into small hollows. Growth of the skin around each hollow forms a 'lid' and a young toad completes its larval life enclosed within each of these pits. When they come out they are tiny replicas of the parents. A few frogs and toads construct nests for their eggs but most of them leave their eggs to the mercy of fish, ducks and many other animals. Only a small proportion of the eggs ever reach maturity.

Reptiles

The Range of Reptile Forms

1) *Seymouria (extinct)*   *7*) *Tuatara*
2) *Tortoise*   *8*) *Crocodile*
3) *Green turtle*   *9*) *Diplodocus (extinct)*
4) *Ichthyosaurus (extinct)*   *10* *Iguanodon (extinct)*
5) *Eastern coral snake*   *11*) *Pteranodon (extinct)*
6) *Sand lizard*   *12* *Dimetrodon (extinct)*

The ancient, clumsy amphibians lived for millions of years, restricted by their mode of reproduction to the vicinity of water. Fossils show that they became better adapted for life on the land – their limbs became stronger for walking and they developed a more water-proof skin. Then, very gradually, they evolved eggs with tough shells. These eggs could contain liquid and the embryos could develop without a free-living larval stage dependent on watery surroundings. The amphibians had evolved into reptiles. The early reptiles were not restricted to damp places and were able to spread comparatively rapidly over the earth. They gradually replaced the amphibians, apart from a few specialised lines which gave rise to modern amphibians.

For about 150 million years the reptiles ruled the world. They branched out into all sorts of habitats – ichthyosaurs and plesiosaurs in the seas, pterodactyls in the air, and the great range of terrestrial dinosaurs.

But many of these branches were evolutionary 'dead ends' – today's reptiles represent only a fraction of the vast number of types alive in Jurassic times, about 150 million years ago. About 100 million years ago the reptiles began to decline and they were replaced as dominant animals by the mammals and birds which arose from different lines of reptiles.

Today's reptiles belong to four orders: Chelonia – turtles and tortoises; Rhynchocephalia – containing only the tuatara of New Zealand; Squamata – the lizards and snakes; and Crocodilia – crocodiles and alligators. The lizards and snakes are the only living reptiles that could be called successful – they are changed quite considerably from their ancestral form. The other groups of living reptiles have remained more or less unchanged for millions of years.

Reptiles are cold blooded animals like the fishes and amphibians. They are most active in warm weather and are commonest in tropical regions. The skin is dry and covered with horny scales.

CHAPTER EIGHTEEN

Feeding and Digestion

THE digestive system of reptiles is very similar to that described in an earlier chapter for the typical vertebrate. Some chelonians – all of which lack teeth – are vegetarians but other living reptiles are carnivorous. Food is seized by the teeth (the jaws in chelonians) and may or may not be broken up before it is swallowed. There are mucous glands in the mouth but no digestion takes place until the food reaches the stomach. Some lizards such as the chameleon use their tongues to capture small prey. The intestine is generally rather short – in accordance with the carnivorous

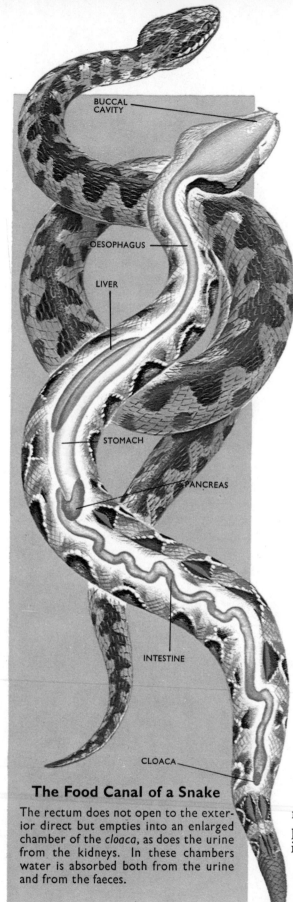

BUCCAL
CAVITY

OESOPHAGUS

LIVER

STOMACH

PANCREAS

INTESTINE

CLOACA

The Food Canal of a Snake

The rectum does not open to the exterior direct but empties into an enlarged chamber of the *cloaca*, as does the urine from the kidneys. In these chambers water is absorbed both from the urine and from the faeces.

habits of the animals.

FEEDING IN SNAKES

The absence of limbs in snakes might make one think that they would have difficulty in catching and consuming food. But this is not so. Special modifications of the skull, jaws, and certain other organs fully compensate for the absence of limbs. In fact, there are no known plant-eating snakes and it is rare, too, for a snake to eat dead food.

The diet of snakes consists of a wide variety of animals (including other snakes). A few of the smaller species feed upon worms, slugs and insects, but most snakes thrive on frogs, lizards, other snakes and small mammals such as rodents. Reports of huge snakes eating pigs and antelopes are often quoted but such cases are comparatively rare.

Most snakes appear to find their food by sight and smell. The continual flickering of the forked tongue serves to collect tiny particles from the air and the ground. Sensitive organs in the roof of the mouth can then detect any smell associated with these particles. Having found its prey, the snake must overpower it before eating it. In the case of small and relatively inactive prey there is no problem, but birds and mammals must first be killed or, at least, paralysed. This is done by constriction (the snake winds its body around its victim and prevents it from breathing) or by the injection of poison. Snake venoms usually act upon the blood and tissues or upon the nervous system. The venoms are produced in modified mucous glands in the mouth.

Not all snakes are poisonous. Many

FANGS

END OF WIND PIPE

TONGUE

A rattle-snake striking. The fangs are outstretched ready to be plunged into the victim. (Inset), The mouth from the front, showing the opening of the wind-pipe between the lower jaws.

have neither poison glands nor fangs, which are special teeth modified for conducting venoms. The largest family of snakes is the *Colubridae* which contains both poisonous and non-poisonous species. The fangs (when present) are relatively short and are not moveable. Snakes of the family *Viperidae* all have large fangs which lie along the roof of the mouth when at rest. The bones of the upper jaw are moveable and, when the snake strikes, they move like levers so that the fangs are pushed forward. Closing of the mouth then forces the fangs into the victim. Small mammals are quickly killed. In the *Elapidae* (Cobras, Mambas, etc. the fangs are quite short and are not moveable but the venom is usually very powerful.

All the snake's teeth are sharp pointed structures not adapted for chewing. All food is swallowed whole therefore, Snakes are normally very slender-bodied creatures but their jaws are so constructed that they can swallow prey of a considerably larger diameter. The two halves of the lower jaw are not fused together but joined by an elastic ligament. At the hind end, the lower jaw is loosely attached to the skull and there is frequently a hinge in the skull which allows the mouth to open even more. As a rule the prey is swallowed head first. The rows of sharp backward pointing teeth catch hold of the animal and the jaws of the snake are gradually moved forward until the prey is completely engulfed. The snake in fact draws itself over its food by means of its teeth. The

The jaw and skull of a rattle-snake.

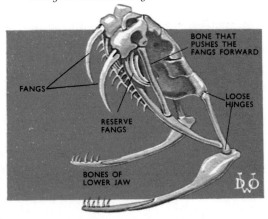

BONE THAT PUSHES THE FANGS FORWARD

FANGS

LOOSE HINGES

RESERVE FANGS

BONES OF LOWER JAW

F

whole region of the mouth and neck is very elastic, so too are the ribs, and the food is moved on into the stomach where digestion goes on as normal. During the process of swallowing, the snake's teeth frequently break, but they are continually being replaced by new rows growing parallel in the gum.

Swallowing a large meal may take some considerable time and a special breathing arrangement is present. The end of the windpipe (*glottis*) can be extended into the floor of the mouth (between the two halves of the lower jaw) and breathing can continue unhindered while the snake feeds.

CHAPTER NINETEEN

Breathing in Reptiles

REPTILES, even the aquatic ones, are air-breathers. Their lungs are considerably more complicated than those of the amphibians, with a much larger internal surface for oxygen absorption. Whereas the amphibians force air into their lungs by throat movements, most reptiles suck air into the lungs. Their ribs are moveable and when they are moved backwards the body cavity is enlarged and a partial vacuum is formed. This is immediately countered by air flowing into the lungs. Snakes have only one fully developed lung – the left one being a small sac with no respiratory function. The breathing mechanism is the same, however. Crocodiles possess a structure rather like the mammalian diaphragm which presumably assists the breathing movements. Tortoises and turtles, however, being encased in a rigid shell cannot use the rib move-ments for breathing. Movements of the head and shoulder girdles, together with the pumping action of the throat, force air into the rather spongy lungs.

The front parts of the lungs are usually better developed than the hind parts as regards respiratory surface. The hind parts tend to be smoother and less folded. In some reptiles the hind parts of the lungs are quite smooth like the air sacs of bird lungs.

Some water-living turtles augment their lung breathing by taking water into special sacs at the hind end of the body. These sacs are well supplied with blood, and oxygen from the water passes into the blood stream. This is the nearest thing in reptiles to the skin breathing of amphibians. Reptiles cannot breathe through their thick, scaly skins.

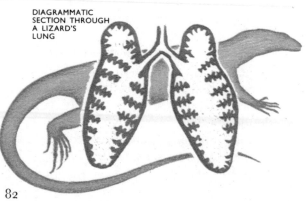

DIAGRAMMATIC SECTION THROUGH A LIZARD'S LUNG

CHAPTER TWENTY

The Nervous System

MODERN reptiles show a great development of the basal parts of the fore-brain. There are large numbers of nervous connections between the thalamus and the cerebral hemispheres. The latter are considerably larger than the optic lobes, showing the increased importance of the hemispheres. The walls of the thalamus are very thick and many of the optic nerve paths end there as well as many in the mid-brain. One thus sees in the reptiles the beginning of the transfer of co-ordinating functions to the fore-brain. This transfer reaches its peak in the mammal whose cerebral hemispheres dwarf and cover the rest of the brain. Although the reptiles cannot be said to be intelligent, they show several behavioural advances over the amphibians.

The huge dinosaurs that lived millions of years ago were not very intelligent. One huge beast some 70 or 80 feet long had a brain little bigger than a walnut to control its body. Many dinosaurs had 'secondary brains' in the hip region. These 'secondary brains' were really swellings of the spinal cord and were associated with the large size of the posterior regions of these animals.

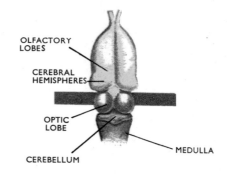

OLFACTORY LOBES

CEREBRAL HEMISPHERES

OPTIC LOBE

CEREBELLUM

MEDULLA

LIZARD BRAIN

The brain is viewed from above and arranged so that the fore-brain/mid-brain junction lies on the red line.

CHAPTER TWENTY-ONE

Reproduction in Reptiles

MOST amphibians have to return to water to breed. Their eggs are soft and jelly-like, lack a supporting shell, and the young, which breathe by means of gills, can live only in water. But whereas amphibians have met with only moderate success in their efforts to colonise land, reptiles have succeeded. To such an extent, in fact, that present day water-dwellers have to return to land in order to breed!

Most reptiles lay eggs, some give birth to live young and a few retain the eggs within their bodies until they are ready to hatch. Reptile eggs show several advances on those of amphibians. The soft substance of the egg is surrounded by a leathery protective shell. This provides the support that a living structure needs on land and also restricts the loss of water to the atmosphere. The eggs are supplied with large quantities of yolk to nourish the developing young, and a special sac, the *allantois*, enables oxygen and carbon dioxide to pass between the embryo and the outside world. Each embryo develops in a fluid-filled sac or *amniotic cavity*, the equivalent of the frog tadpole's pond. The young reptile that hatches from the egg is a miniature of the adult and not a larval form like the amphibian tadpole.

Except in lizards, there is usually little difference in the appearance of male and female reptiles of the same species. Amongst the crocodiles, for example the American alligator, the difference is merely one of size. The male is often larger and heavier than the female after about the sixth year. Amongst turtles there are rarely differences in colour and often not in size, but when there are size differences the female is usually the larger, though the male has a relatively

Female turtles come on land to lay their eggs, usually burying them in the sand of the shore. The young turtles are easy prey for sea-birds until they reach the water's edge.

larger tail. In snakes the two sexes are very much alike, and the production of scent by special glands apparently serves as a means of recognition. It is among lizards, however, that striking sexual differences, approaching those of some fishes, are to be found. They may be permanent structural features, or momentary or seasonal changes in appearance. A male Owen's chameleon has three large pointed horns on its head, whereas the female has one only; these are permanent features, as are the vivid colours of the throat and underside of male spiny lizards. Male agamids and iguanids are well known for their ability to become momentarily brightly coloured. In the breeding season the male collared lizard takes on striking colours. At this time male lizards also defend their territories ferociously, driving away male intruders by means of violent attacks.

Since reptiles produce eggs that have shells, fertilization must be internal and takes place high up in the reproductive system, beyond the shell-producing glands. Some means of introducing the sperm is also necessary and male reptiles have well developed structures serving this purpose.

Some female turtles, snakes and lizards are able to store the sperm received during pairing. Thus several successive batches of young may be produced as the result of a single act of pairing. Fertilization need not follow pairing immediately, therefore. Diamondback terrapins have been known to lay fertile eggs four years after pairing has taken place, and one snake, *Leptodeira*, as long as five years after pairing.

All crocodiles and turtles lay eggs, so far as is known. The majority of snakes and lizards also lay eggs, but others give birth to live young. The viviparous lizard (*Lacerta vivipara*) is remarkable in that it normally produces live young, yet over part of its range – in the Pyrenees – it lays eggs. Amongst egg-laying reptiles the number of eggs laid varies from one to over a hundred. The monitor lizards and horned toads may lay thirty or more, but most lizards lay fifteen or less. Geckos and iguanids often lay a solitary egg. Snakes (particularly pythons) and turtles are the most prolific, some snakes laying over a hundred eggs and some sea turtles producing two hundred.

Nest building is rarely very elaborate, and more often than not a hole in the ground or a pile of waste vegetable matter will suffice, the heat of the fermenting mass speeding up the hatching. Female turtles are well known for their habit of returning to land in order to lay their eggs – often, it seems, to the same sandy beach, and the one on which they themselves hatched. Whereas some turtles deposit

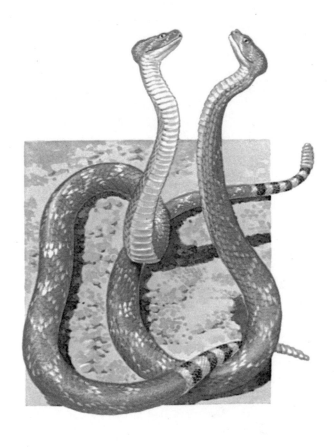

The reproductive organs of a lizard. The male (left) has two testes whose ducts open into the cloaca. The female has two ovaries (one only shown) that open similarly.

Two male rattlesnakes in 'combat dance' – a form of display conducted in front of a female. (Below) Snakes hatching from their eggs.

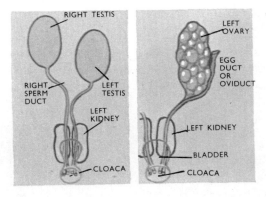

their eggs in a shallow depression and hardly bother to conceal them, others take great pains, first digging a deep hole with their flippers, before depositing the eggs. Sand is then thrown over them until they are buried and the site of the nest is concealed by more loose sand. This process may be so effective that an onlooker has been unable to find the eggs after several hours' digging!

Many egg-laying snakes guard their eggs by remaining curled around them. Some put up a vigorous defence against intruders. It is thought that male and female cobras take it in turn to guard the eggs and there is evidence that one species of python actually incubates them, having a body temperature several degrees above that of the surroundings. However, parental care in snakes goes little beyond defence of the eggs, for the parents leave the young to fend for themselves after hatching.

Many females of some species have the habit of congregating in one place, to lay. The European grass snake is famous for this habit and sometimes several thousand eggs are found together. This snake, like many others, lays its eggs where there is an abundance of rotting plant material, the heat of the fermenting mass increasing their rate of development.

The female American alligator constructs a large nest as much as seven feet across and three feet high. The nest is a mound constructed of decaying plants, freshly collected leaves and other vegetable matter. A hollow in the centre is scooped out and lined with mud and water plants. She deposits her eggs (approximately thirty to seventy in number), turning round in the hollow as she lays, and covers them with mud and other water plants. The whole of the nest is then smoothed over by the great body of the alligator. The nest is carefully guarded and even watered during dry weather. Incubation takes about nine weeks. Sounds from the young, prior to hatching, provide the signal for the female to bite the top off the nest so that they may escape.

The American Alligator lays perhaps 50 eggs in a mound of mud and vegetation. The mound is completely covered until the eggs hatch. The mother hears the young and opens up the nest.

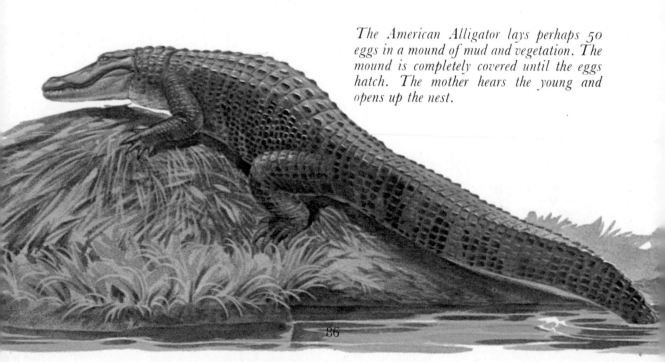

Birds

INTRODUCTION

The most noticeable and characteristic features of birds are their feathers. Most of them are able to fly – the fore-limbs are modified as wings – and all of them lay eggs. The birds share with the mammals the ability to maintain a high, constant body temperature and, unlike the reptiles, they can be active at all temperatures.

The oldest known bird is called *Archaeopteryx* and it lived some 140 million years ago. Two fairly complete fossils have been found and they show that *Archaeopteryx* had a long, lizard-like skeleton with a tail. The skull too was lizard-like and carried teeth. But the creature was covered in feathers and the front limbs were modified as wings. It was therefore a true bird. The other features, including claws on the wings, show clearly that it was descended from reptiles but there is a big gap between the basic reptile stock and *Archaeopteryx* and the intermediate stages in the evolution of birds can only be guessed at. There obviously must have been feathered creatures before *Archaeopteryx* but no fossils have yet been found. It is clear, however, that the birds did not evolve from the flying pterodactyls – the skeletons of these were very different from that of *Archaeopteryx*.

The development of feathers from the reptile scales was undoubtedly a major factor in the ability of birds to maintain a high body temperature. The use of feathers for flight presumably came later. It is believed that the birds arose from a group of tree-living reptiles which started to glide from tree to tree as the wing feathers became larger.

Bird fossils are relatively rare, for these animals do not live in places where they are likely to be preserved. A few fossils, however, have been discovered showing the gradual evolution and radiation of modern birds. The teeth and tail have been lost and the only visible signs of their reptilian ancestry are the scales on the legs and the habit of laying eggs.

The modern birds are extremely successful animals and, apart from their mastery of the air, they have colonised a wide variety of terrestrial habitats. The variety of habitats and habits is reflected in a number of interesting modifications of the

The first fossil Archaeopteryx *found is kept in the Natural History Museum, London. A second, discovered in 1877, is kept in Berlin.*

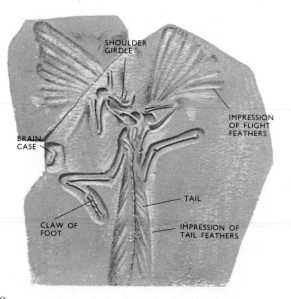

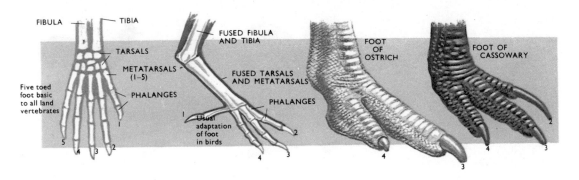

FIBULA — TIBIA

Five toed foot basic to all land vertebrates

TARSALS

METATARSALS (1-5)

PHALANGES

5 4 3 2 1

FUSED FIBULA AND TIBIA

FUSED TARSALS AND METATARSALS

PHALANGES

Usual adaptation of foot in birds

1 4 3 2

FOOT OF OSTRICH

4 3

FOOT OF CASSOWARY

4 3 2

feet and it is usually possible to say quite a lot about the habits of a bird from a quick look at its feet.

THE FEET OF BIRDS

A foot with five toes is basic to all land vertebrates. But most birds have feet with four toes; the fifth has gone without trace. The first (big) toe, called the *hallux*, is usually turned towards the rear. Working in opposition to the other three, it provides an excellent mechanism for perching or – in the case of flesh-eating birds – for grasping and carrying prey. Alternatively, the backward pointing hallux may be very long and straight as in larks and wagtails. These birds spend a lot of time running over flat ground and the long hallux helps their stance.

The large flightless birds, in the majority of cases, have lost their first toes. They do not need a perching foot of any kind, for example, the Australian cassowaries. The 8-foot-tall ostrich, largest of living birds, has not only lost the first toe but the second as well. It runs using just the third and fourth toes.

In woodpeckers, cuckoos, parrots and toucans, the fourth toe as well as the first, may be turned backwards. The result is a strong, stable climbing and perching mechanism which can also be used for feeding purposes.

This condition is known as *zygodactyl*. One family of birds, the trogons, also have two toes facing forwards and two backwards. But it is the second toe that has moved to the back, not the fourth. This is the *heterodactyl* condition.

Owls, rollers and the osprey have a flexible fourth toe which, though normally facing forwards, can also be turned backwards. The condition is a *semi-zygodactyl* one. In contrast, swifts have a flexible first toe which can be moved forwards (*pamprodactyl*). Using their four forward projecting toes, they hang from small projections; their feet are too feeble for normal perching.

In the *syndactylous* condition, toes are fused for some of their length. Kingfishers, matmots and the West Indian todies have all three front toes partially joined; a scoop-like structure is formed, excellent for digging nests in the ground.

Water birds engaged in swimming and diving may have flaps of skin between the toes, forming a webbed foot. The webbed feet act as paddles, presenting a large surface area to push against the water. They may also be used for steering.

Usually only the front three toes are webbed and the hind toe (i.e. the first toe) is reduced in size as in ducks and geese. But some web-footed birds – cormorants and pelicans for instance – have the first toe brought into a for-

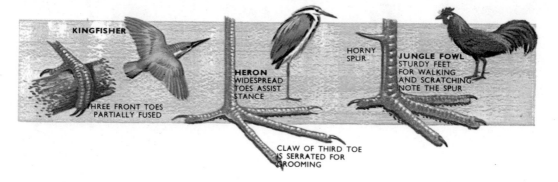

KINGFISHER

THREE FRONT TOES PARTIALLY FUSED

HERON
WIDESPREAD TOES ASSIST STANCE

CLAW OF THIRD TOE IS SERRATED FOR GROOMING

HORNY SPUR

JUNGLE FOWL
STURDY FEET FOR WALKING AND SCRATCHING. NOTE THE SPUR

ward position and it, too, is webbed.

Birds with webbed feet are ungainly and clumsy walkers on land. Coots, grebes and phalaropes – also water birds – instead of a web, have each of the three front toes provided with a scalloped fringe of skin (*lobate webbing*). This extra surface area facilitates swimming but, because each toe is free, the birds can walk equally as well.

Perhaps the best swimmers of all are the divers and the grebes. The diver's webbed and the grebe's lobate feet are set far back on their bodies – just as the propellers of a boat are at the rear. In the diver, it is only the feet which project beyond the body. Leg bones above the ankle are encased within.

Birds which walk over soft mud flats tend to have long toes, well spread out, so that weight is evenly distributed, e.g. heron, curlew. The jaçanas have particularly long toes and walk unconcernedly over floating leaves.

Chickens and gamebirds spend a lot of time on the ground scratching about for food. Their feet are sturdy with three strong toes in front; the hind toe usually remains small. The toes have blunt claws used for scratching the ground; just above the first toe there may be a horny spur for fighting. Ptarmigans – arctic grouse – have their toes covered in warm feathers.

The claw of the third (middle) toe of a few birds – herons, owls, bitterns and nightjars – has a comb-like serrated edge used for grooming and removing slime from feathers.

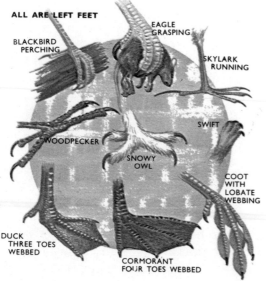

ALL ARE LEFT FEET

BLACKBIRD PERCHING

EAGLE GRASPING

SKYLARK RUNNING

WOODPECKER

SNOWY OWL

SWIFT

COOT WITH LOBATE WEBBING

DUCK THREE TOES WEBBED

CORMORANT FOUR TOES WEBBED

Top: The three forward toes and one rear toe provide mechanisms for perching, grasping or running. Middle: In the woodpecker and other birds the second toe points backwards as well as the first. The owl can if necessary rotate its second toe backwards; the swift in contrast can rotate its first toe forward. Bottom: Webbing of feet in duck, cormorant and coot.

90

CHAPTER TWENTY-TWO

Feathers and Flight

THERE is little superficial likeness between soft, downy bird's feathers and the tough scales that plate the bodies of many reptiles. Yet it is from just such hard scales that feathers probably evolved.

Today, the colour of a bird's feathers is important for protective camouflage, and also for courtship displays at times of mating. The moulting of old feathers accompanied by replacement with new ones may take place throughout the year but in birds of temperate climates it is usually seasonal – once during the spring and then again in the autumn.

Types of Feather

Feathers are made of *keratin*, a horny substance produced by the upper layers of the skin. There are four types of feather, simple *down feathers* and

Colour and Feathers

Some feathers are coloured by pigments contained inside them. *Melanins* are particularly important, giving blacks and all shades of brown. *Carotenoids* give reds, yellows and oranges. When no pigment is present all the light is reflected and the feathers appear white.

Other feathers have a glossy, dark-coloured sheen (*iridescence*) caused by a special surface layer of keratin.

Colour may be important in blending the bird with its background. Mottling is especially useful as it breaks up the distinctive outline of the bird when it is at rest. Light-coloured plumage reflects the sun's rays and in deserts is probably a protection against excessive heat.

Distinct colouring probably helps birds to recognize other members of their own species. Birds that live in flocks, such as starlings and rooks, are always very conspicuously coloured. Brightly coloured plumage of birds such as male peacocks and pheasants are used for courtship displays.

The Mandarin duck shows sexual dichromatism *– the plumage of the male and female differs in colour. Bright feathers are displayed at times of mating.*

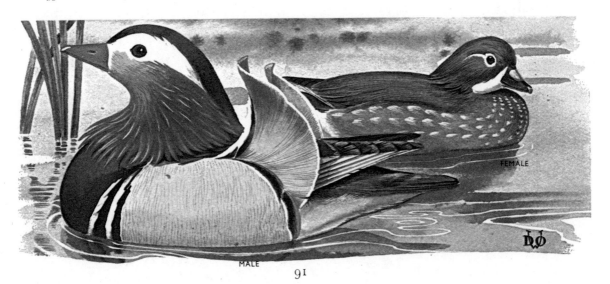

MALE

FEMALE

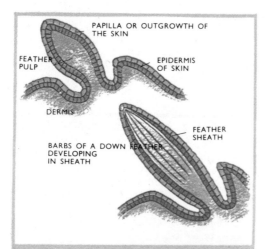

PAPILLA OR OUTGROWTH OF THE SKIN

FEATHER PULP

EPIDERMIS OF SKIN

DERMIS

FEATHER SHEATH

BARBS OF A DOWN FEATHER DEVELOPING IN SHEATH

Formation of a down feather. Each quill develops inside a sheath and divides at its far end into numerous barbs. The barbs are freed by the breakdown of the sheath. Below, the barbs of contour feathers do not grow like branches on a tree. They first form on a collar of tissue inside the skin and migrate up the main shaft.

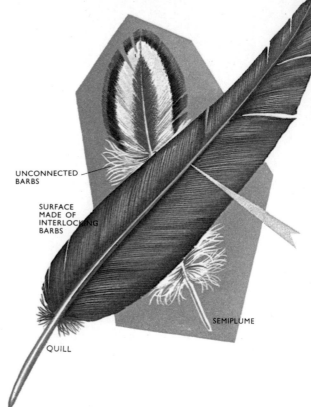

UNCONNECTED BARBS

SURFACE MADE OF INTERLOCKING BARBS

QUILL

SEMIPLUME

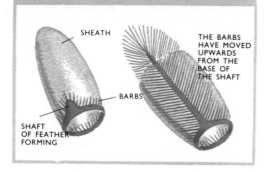

SHEATH

BARBS

SHAFT OF FEATHER FORMING

THE BARBS HAVE MOVED UPWARDS FROM THE BASE OF THE SHAFT

Down feathers insulate young chicks. In adult birds they are partially replaced by contour feathers.

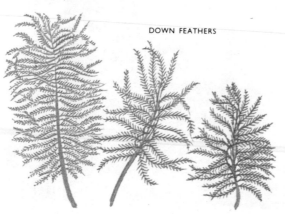

DOWN FEATHERS

pin-feathers (filoplumes), more complex *contour feathers*, and specialized *powder-down* feathers.

Contour feathers are large and sheathe the body of the bird, as well as covering the tail and wings. The actual *quill* of the feather is the section of the stem which remains embedded in the skin. It is usually hollow with two small openings, one at its base and one where the quill perforates the skin surface.

The rest of the contour feather above the skin's surface is called the *vane;* it consists of a central, solid shaft extending from the quill and a very large number of small branches (*barbs*) coming off from either side.

The barbs are so closely packed together that they appear to form a continuous surface. In actual fact they are separate units, though each one is attached to its neighbours by a series of hooked and notched *barbules*.

Down feathers are much smaller and simpler. The quill is very small and at the surface, instead of continuing as a main stem, it divides to form a spray of slender branches. The fluffy coats of young chicks are made up entirely of down feathers.

Contour feathers are light with a large surface area made of interlocking barbs. Some contour feathers, used for insulation, develop without the barbs connected; they are fluffy and are called semiplumes.

SHAFT

BARBS

BARBULES

Pin-feathers are even simpler. They consist of just the quill and a short stem which divides at the top into a bunch of small barbs. Powder-down feathers are possessed by only some birds, e.g. Bitterns, Herons, some Hawks. They break down into a powder useful for removing slime and dirt from the rest of the plumage.

Feather and Function

Contour feathers, fitted to the wings and tails of birds, provide a large surface area to push against the air during flight. The sheath of smaller contour feathers formed over the whole body gives the bird a streamlined shape essential for movement through the air. The smooth, flat surfaces of the contour feathers are formed by the tightly linked barbs. If the barbs become disarranged by

unhooking of the barbules, the birds' preening action soon repairs them. For birds which do not fly, it is not important to have smooth, streamlined feathers. Ostriches for instance have plume-like contour feathers, known from their use as decorations.

Down feathers are concerned with insulation of the body from the cold. They help trap a layer of air against the skin. In adult birds they are not usually conspicuous as they are covered by the contour feathers.

Feathers can be moved by the action of muscles just as the hairs that cover mammals can be moved. Ruffling of

Magnified view of barbules. Hooked barbules on the top surface of each barb interlock with notched barbules suspended from the bottom surface.

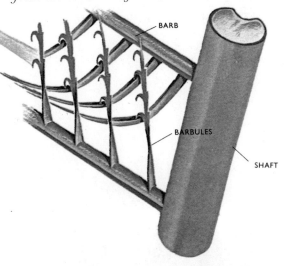

BARB

BARBULES

SHAFT

feathers, for instance, can take place during cold weather (the additional trapped air gives extra warmth) and the position of contour feathers on the wings and on the tail can be controlled in flight.

Again like hairs, feathers are supplied with nerve fibres and can be used as organs of touch. Birds that fly at night have very sensitive hair-like feathers on their faces rather like the 'whiskers' of cats.

Swimming birds protect their feathers from the water by a coating of oil. The oil comes from a special oil gland at the base of the tail and is spread over the feathers by preening with the beak. A few birds use their feathers for making noises during flight. The Snipe's 'bleat' as it circles over its marshland home is caused by the air vibrating special tail feathers. The sound is probably used as a warning noise. The Woodcock which flies at night 'whistles' as air passes through peculiarly constructed contour feathers on the wing. It is probable that this sound acts as a position marker for others.

Flight

Two forces must act on a body in order that it can move through the

Owls have whisker-like feathers very sensitive to touch.
The flight feathers have delicate filaments at their edges to ensure silent flight.

WHITE-FACED
SCOPS

air. These are *thrust* and *lift*. The propellers or jets of an aircraft provide thrust and so produce movement forwards. Each wing has a curved upper surface and as it is moved through the air the airstream is deflected up over this curved surface. It is 'stretched out', therefore, relative to the airstream below the wing. So the pressure immediately above the wing is reduced and the wing tends to rise. It is *lifted*. By tilting the wings so that the leading edge is above the trailing one, the pressure on the undersurface is increased and so extra lift is obtained. Wing slots ensure that the air flow over the upper surface remains smooth.

Birds make use of exactly the same principles for flight although things are a little more complex because the bird's wing has to provide forward motion as well as lift. The wing itself is a modification of a five-fingered limb. The wrist and hand bones are reduced and only the second finger is well developed. The first digit (thumb) stands apart and carries the feathers of the alula which acts as a slotting device. The third finger is a single rod while the fourth and fifth are absent. The large feathers, *primaries*, are attached to the back edge of the hand, while the smaller feathers are placed on the forearm and upper arm. The feathers are all designed with a stiff leading edge and a taper to the back. They overlap each other on the wings and produce a rigid surface to meet the air stream. The shape and curvature of the wing is altered by changing the positions of the feathers by means of muscles and tendons to which all the feathers are attached.

Both thrust and lift are obtained by flapping the wings up and down. The

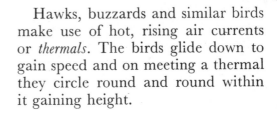

An Albatross uses gusts of wind and the variable wind speed at different levels to glide above the sea surface.

wings can be rotated to increase the effectiveness of the downward stroke which is the power-producing stroke. Before the wing tips have reached the lowest point in the downstroke each wing is bent at the wrist so that this part of the wing begins the upstroke. The resistance of the wing to the air as it passes upwards is thus kept to a minimum.

Changes of direction are made both by using the tail as a rudder and by changing the shape and position of one wing so that its lift and speed are reduced or increased.

Besides flapping flight, many birds are able to glide and soar. Seagulls and albatross glide over the waves, making use of gusts of wind and variable wind speeds at different levels. They gain speed by gliding down-wind and gain height by turning into a gust. At the same time they move into the faster moving air further above the disturbed sea surface.

Feathers are arranged on the hind borders of the wing bones. The wing is derived from a typical five-fingered limb by reduction of the wrist and hand bones and the loss of two fingers.

Hawks, buzzards and similar birds make use of hot, rising air currents or *thermals*. The birds glide down to gain speed and on meeting a thermal they circle round and round within it gaining height.

Vultures and hawks soar slowly on thermals. This is made possible by broad, well-slotted wings.

CHAPTER TWENTY-THREE

Feeding and Digestion

MODERN birds are all toothless but the development of the horny beak has partly made up for this lack. The beak is very hard and strong in some birds and the jaws are very powerful – parrots can actually crack Brazil nuts which defeat many humans! But the beak is not, however, a complete substitute for teeth.

Although the beak is used for biting, tearing or cracking seeds, most mastication of the food takes place internally. But the beak has largely taken the place of the forelimbs. In birds these structures are adapted as wings. They no longer can be used for grasping, clutching, or conveying food to the mouth as in other upright creatures. The beak, sometimes with the help of the feet, must do the necessary probing and plucking and holding; it also must be used for personal cleaning and grooming as well as carrying out such functions as nest-building and feeding the young.

The design of a beak reflects the predominant diet of the bird in ques-tion. As the food consumed by birds is so variable – from flesh of other ani-mals to the nectar of flowers – so the variety of beak is correspondingly enormous. Specialized hunting birds have sharp hooked beaks suitable for tearing flesh. These flesh-eaters include the eagles, hawks, falcons and owls. Scavenging birds such as vultures may also have hooked beaks; alternatively the beak may be long and stout – crows and the maribou. Birds like the heron, with fish as a staple diet, are equipped with a long, dagger-like beak. Ex-amples are the terns, kingfisher, the guillemots and the gannet. Beneath the long tapering beak of the pelican, loose skin of the throat can be dis-tended into a dip net for receiving fish. The oyster-catcher has a long, blunt, vertically flattened bill well adapted to opening oysters, probing deep in mud or prising limpets from rocks.

Seed-eating birds such as finches, buntings and siskins have short, thick strong beaks. Hard outer seed cases

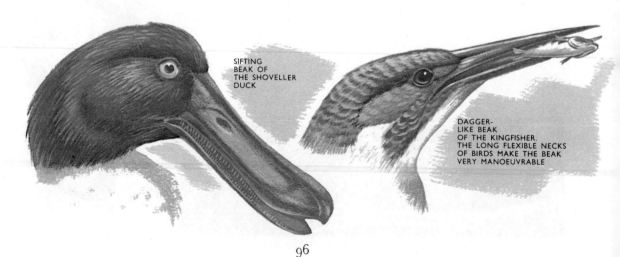

SIFTING BEAK OF THE SHOVELLER DUCK

DAGGER-LIKE BEAK OF THE KINGFISHER. THE LONG FLEXIBLE NECKS OF BIRDS MAKE THE BEAK VERY MANOEUVRABLE

"ALL-PURPOSES" BEAK OF THE ROOK. LONG AND STOUT, IT IS USED FOR DEVOURING A VARIETY OF FOODS – INSECTS, CARRION, FIELD MICE AS WELL AS FRUIT AND GRAIN

SHARP-EDGED HOOKED BEAK OF FLESH-DEVOURING FALCON

may have to be cracked; the stout beaks exert great pressure – just like the area near the hinge of a pair of nutcrackers. These beaks are also excellent for nipping off young buds. Another seed eater, the cross-bill, has the upper and lower halves of its beak overlapping. With this device it can pick up the smallest seeds without difficulty.

Blackbirds, thrushes, starlings and many other birds have moderately long beaks. They are not long enough to fish but sufficient for probing for worms, eating molluscs, and grubs, and pecking at soft fruits.

Wading birds that probe for worms and molluscs in soft mud flats have long beaks which are flattened sideways and sometimes curved downwards. The beaks are well provided with nerves at the tips and are very sensitive. Characteristic waders are the sandpipers, greenshanks, redshanks and curlews.

Ducks have broad beaks flattened downwards and deeply grooved inside; they are used for sifting worms and small aquatic animals from mud and water, but will also devour herbage, grain and berries. An extreme example of the sifting type of bill is found in the shovellers. Such birds have large, flattened, spatulate beaks which are provided with bristle-like structures about the edges. These

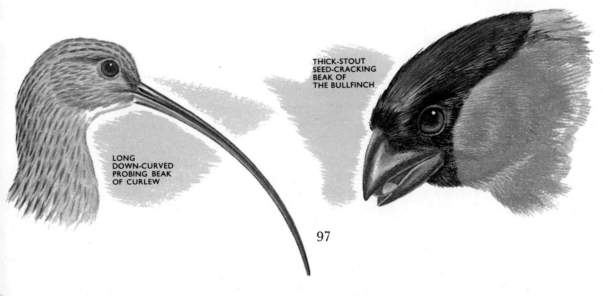

LONG DOWN-CURVED PROBING BEAK OF CURLEW

THICK-STOUT SEED-CRACKING BEAK OF THE BULLFINCH

97

HUMMING BIRD

The humming birds feed on nectar. They have a preference for flowers with tubular heads, inserting their beaks into the opening and lapping the nectar with their tongues. The length of the bills varies with the size of the flowers visited.

TOCO TOUCAN

Why the toucan's bill should be quite as long is something of a mystery. Certainly the bird's reach is considerably extended. The bill, made of horny skin covering a delicate meshwork of bone, is not so heavy as it looks.

retain edible material as mud is squeezed from the bill. The spoonbills have spatulate tips to their flattened beaks. These birds wade along with the beak half immersed in water snapping up anything edible. Numerous nerve endings are present in the tip, making it very sensitive.

Flamingoes have a unique feeding mechanism. Their beaks are curved right over so that when immersed in

the water, the top bill is bottom-most. The pumping action of the lower bill drives mud and water through slits in the top bill. Small edible creatures – algae, diatoms, worms, larvae, crustaceans – are filtered out by tooth-like projections from the tongue.

Avocets are famous for their long strongly upturned bills. They wade along, with jaws open, sweeping the bill from side to side either at the surface of the water or near the bottom. Small invertebrate creatures are eaten and also small fishes and amphibians.

The woodpeckers have long, strong, chisel-like beaks. The beak actually bores into the bark of trees and a long protrusible tongue laps up the exposed insects. Tree-creepers also have long beaks but they are much feebler. They do not attack the bark but only probe into its crevices.

Humming birds have a diet of nectar. Their beaks, which often curve downwards, are slender and thin. They vary in length according to the size of the flowers visited. The humming bird hovers motionless over a flower and inserts its beak inside the petals. The tongue, which can be extended beyond the tip of the beak, either has a tubular tip for sucking or is brushy.

Toucans have enormous beaks and the cutting edges are serrated. Their diet consists of succulent fruits. Certainly the length of the beak helps the bird reach out for inaccessible fruit but need it be quite the size it is? One theory is that the beak evolved for eating some fruit or insect that no longer exists. Perhaps they are used in courtship displays or as recognition marks between species.

Contrasting in size are the minute beaks of the swallows, swifts and night jars. These birds catch insects on the wing, flying forward with their very wide mouths apart. No probing is necessary and the function of the beak is relegated to grooming.

One bird, the woodpecker finch of the Galapagos Archipelago, uses its beak for handling a tool – just as Man uses his hands for controlling a variety of instruments. The 'tool' of this extraordinary finch is a cactus spine; with it, insects are probed from beneath the bark of trees.

The Alimentary Canal

The digestive system of birds is highly specialised. The long, horny tongue moves the food around in the mouth, ensuring that it is well moistened with saliva. The sense of taste is thought to be very poor in birds. In some of the seed-eaters the saliva is believed to contain enzymes which start to break down the starches in the food. From the mouth, the food passes into the crop – a swelling of the lower part of the oesophagus. This is often large, particularly in birds that eat grain, and the food is partly broken up by its storage there. The stomach is divided into two parts,

The flamingo is a unique feeder. When the bent beak is immersed in water, the top bill becomes bottom-most. Water is pumped by the lower bill through slits in the upper bill. The tongue filters food out of the water.

Puffins and their relatives (auks and razorbills) live off fish. The broad bill of the puffin can carry several fish at once. The bird bites deeply into each caught fish preventing its escape.

Left: Nostrils are usually in the middle or at the base of the beak. But the Kiwi, that hunts by smell, has them at the tip. Middle: Parrots have the upper mandible hinged at the base of the skull; this mechanism provides them with the greatest leverage of all birds. Right: the fish-eating skimmer; the lower, longer bill is submerged in the sea. When a fish is located the upper bill clamps down.

KIWI – NOSTRILS AT THE EXTREME TIP OF BILL

MACAW – THE STRONG HOOKED BILL CAN BE USED AS A THIRD LEG

SKIMMER

SHORTER UPPER BILL IS HELD OUT OF THE WATER

LONG, LOWER BILL IS IMMERSED IN THE WATER

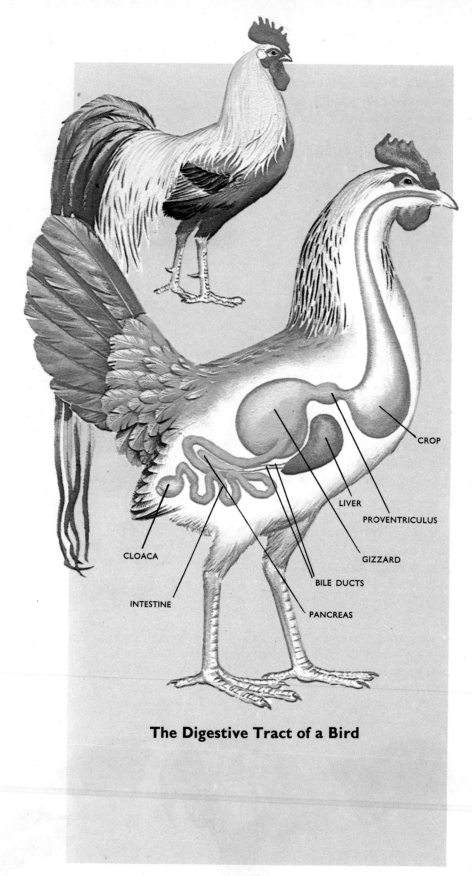

CROP

LIVER

PROVENTRICULUS

CLOACA

GIZZARD

BILE DUCTS

INTESTINE

PANCREAS

The Digestive Tract of a Bird

the *proventriculus* and the gizzard. The former produces enzymes and the food, which is then thoroughly moistened and partly broken down, is ground up in the gizzard which has a thick, powerful and muscular wall. In carnivorous birds the gizzard is less muscular. Bile and the pancreatic juices are poured onto the food in the small intestine where digestion is completed. The cloaca is divided into chambers and much of the water in the faeces and from the urine is absorbed there.

CHAPTER TWENTY-FOUR

Breathing in Birds

BIRDS have a higher body temperature than that of any other animal. This allows the tissues to work at a high rate. They therefore require large quantities of oxygen, particularly for such an activity as flying. To satisfy the great demands of the tissues an elaborate system of air sacs is developed. The lungs are small but tubes from them lead to air sacs, some of which invade even the hollow cavities of bones. Every lung tube, even the finer branches, is open. They do not end in blind sacs as in mammals. Air can pass through the lungs into the air sacs at inspiration and out again at expiration. The lung capillaries are thus in contact with a continuous supply of oxygen. The walls of the air sacs are smooth and have a poor blood supply, so that little or no respiratory exchange takes place across them. The air sacs may be divided into two groups: one posterior (rear) set consisting of two pairs (see illustration) and an anterior (front) set consisting of two pairs and a single sac.

At rest the respiratory movements are produced by the rib muscles (intercostals) and the abdominal muscles. The former contract to move the ribs and breastbone and so enlarge the body cavity. Air passes in through the lung to the posterior group of air sacs. The abdominal muscles act to reduce the size of the body cavity so that air passes from the posterior air sacs through the lungs into the anterior sacs. From there it may pass to the exterior. During flight the action of the large breast muscles (*pectorals*) produces the air flow in and out of the lungs by lowering and raising the breastbone. The flight muscles generate large quantities of heat during flying, and since birds lack sweat glands it is probable that the air sacs are important regulators of the body temperature through cooling.

The lungs of birds are small. But accessory air sacs act as gigantic pumps and circulate large quantities of air.

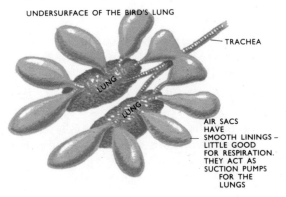

UNDERSURFACE OF THE BIRD'S LUNG

TRACHEA

LUNG

LUNG

AIR SACS HAVE SMOOTH LININGS — LITTLE GOOD FOR RESPIRATION. THEY ACT AS SUCTION PUMPS FOR THE LUNGS

CHAPTER TWENTY-FIVE

The Nervous System

THE brain in birds is similar to that of reptiles except that the olfactory part of the fore-brain is very small; smell is unimportant in birds. The cerebral hemispheres are relatively larger and the whole brain is rather bunched up from front to back but the general pattern is clear. The mid-brain and optic lobes are still well developed and have many nervous connections with the cerebral hemisphere and the motor systems since sight plays a very important part in the life of birds. As is to be expected, the cerebellum is highly developed to control the balance and position of the bird when flying. Much of this development has undoubtedly been made possible by the constant high temperature maintained by the birds.

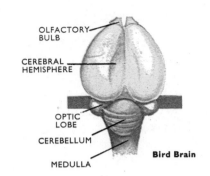

The brain is viewed from above and arranged so that the fore-brain/mid-brain junction lies on the red line.

CHAPTER TWENTY-SIX

Reproduction and Nest Building

BIRDS are highly industrious creatures. From dawn until dusk their continuous activity can be witnessed. Their reproductive and associated behaviour is particularly intense and noticeable. Many birds undertake long migratory flights in order to reach their breeding grounds, and pairing is often preceded by courtship and display ceremonies, more elaborate than are found in any other animals, except possibly man. During the display, 'gifts' such as stones (e.g. Adelie penguins) or weeds (e.g. Great Crested Grebe) may be offered by the male to the female or by the two birds to each other. The spreading of wings and tail feathers in characteristic positions by the male may display colours not normally seen and which act as signals having special significance to the female. She may reply with her own set of signals. Often the male is more brightly coloured. With this may be associated special structures such as a comb (e.g. domestic fowl) or the extraordinary growth of tail feathers, so heavy in some instances that the bird is then scarcely capable of flight!

Some birds keep the same pairs for a year, others pair for the breeding season only, whilst some come together solely for the purpose of mating. Yet others usually pair for life (e.g. Jackdaws). A nesting site may be found be-

King and Emperor Penguins build no nest, but incubate their eggs holding them off the ground between their feet.

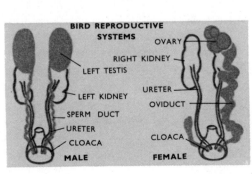

fore or after pairing. Trees, hollow cavities in walls, pipes, cliff-ledges, and hollow depressions in the ground or in a tree branch are amongst the variety of nesting places.

Not all birds build nests, yet nest-building is a most characteristic activity. Material for the nest may be obtained from the immediate surroundings of the nesting site or it may be brought from considerable distances. Swallows will collect mud several hundred yards from the nest, whereas a swan uses grass, water-plants etc., that are close to hand. The nest may be constructed by one or both birds and the same nesting site may be used several years running, new material being added on top of the old nest, so that eventually a nest of massive size is produced. Such are the nests of herons. Owls and falcons make no nest but use tree hollows or merely scrape a hollow depression on a ledge or somewhere similar. They may also take over the old nests of other birds. The social weavers of South Africa build enormous communal nests, and as many as three hundred pairs may

live in the same 'apartment house'.

Common building materials are twigs, leaves, dry grass, moss, lichens, mud and feathers. In many instances the nest consists of an outer layer of coarse material – twigs, sticks, straw and the like – while the inner lining is of a finer, softer nature – hair, wool, feathers etc. Usually the bird uses its bill to fix building material in place whilst the actual shaping of the nest is done with the feet, wings and body. A few birds, such as the weavers, many of which build hanging nests made of grass and palm fibres, actually tie the strands into knots.

The eggs are generally oval in shape with one end blunter than the other. Birds are not as prolific as reptiles, though the number of eggs varies from species to species and between separate clutches of the same species. Four to six is a normal clutch for most of the perching birds (Robin, Sparrow,

The Edible-nest Swiftlets of Malaya and Indochina build their delicate cup-shaped nests entirely of saliva.

A male Red-plumed Bird of Paradise (right) displays to the less brightly coloured female (top left). (bottom left) A male Little King Bird of Paradise.

Rook, etc.), and many others. The Golden Eagle lays two eggs. Pheasants and partridges may lay up to fifteen and ostriches up to twenty.

Whereas reptile eggs are usually a dirty white or cream colour, those of many birds are beautifully marked, often blending remarkably with the background. The Ringed Plover constructs no nest – its eggs are laid among pebbles and stone which they match so closely that they are difficult to see. The eggs of many birds are white, however (e.g. Wryneck, Owls, Petrels, Swift), whilst in others the eggs are brightly speckled. Possibly their colour helps to maintain the broody state of the parents, for experiments in which eggs of the wrong colours have been placed in the nest resulted in the broody bird leaving.

Each egg has a rich supply of yolk for the developing embryo, though the proportion is not as high as in reptiles (e.g. turtles) – presumably this is related to their more rapid development. Birds, like mammals, are warm-blooded and the developing egg must be kept warm. This is performed by one or both of the parents (usually the female) who incubates them while 'sitting on the nest'. Special bare patches of skin – the brood patches – are well supplied with blood and they are applied closely to the eggs. King and Emperor Penguins have a unique way of incubating their eggs, holding them off the ice or the cold ground with their feet.

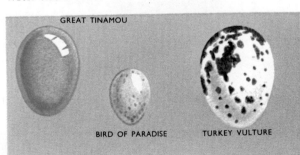

GREAT TINAMOU

BIRD OF PARADISE   TURKEY VULTURE

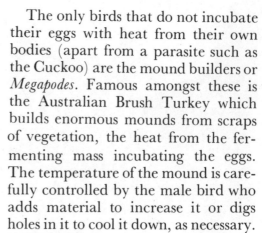

The only birds that do not incubate their eggs with heat from their own bodies (apart from a parasite such as the Cuckoo) are the mound builders or *Megapodes*. Famous amongst these is the Australian Brush Turkey which builds enormous mounds from scraps of vegetation, the heat from the fermenting mass incubating the eggs. The temperature of the mound is carefully controlled by the male bird who adds material to increase it or digs holes in it to cool it down, as necessary.

Parental care reaches an extremely high level in birds. Not only are the eggs incubated by the adults but the young, of necessity, are provisioned and cared for as well. The young break out of their shells by means of an egg-tooth or *caruncle* on top of the bill. They are kept warm by the heat from the parents' bodies. In some instances (e.g. ducks, geese, turkeys) the chicks are able to run actively and peck for food a day or two after hatching, but, generally speaking, they are helpless and quite dependent on the parents.

The adult birds spend a large part of each day collecting insects and their larvae, worms and other suitable food (fish in the case of sea birds) for the nestlings. Adult pigeons produce a curd-like milk in their crops with which to feed the young. Nestlings may consume their own weight of food each day. It seems that the noise they make on the return of the parents to the nest, and the bright colours of the inside of their mouths, stimulate the parents into feeding them. Besides providing food the adult birds also clean the nest, removing faeces and other unwanted material. They will also feign injury or walk away from the nest in an attempt to distract the attentions of an intruder or a would-be predator from the nestlings.

(*Above*) *Parental care reaches an extremely high level in birds. Here a male Golden Oriole adult feeds its young.* (*Below*) *The Australian Brush Turkey builds an enormous mound from scraps of vegetation. Heat from the fermenting mass incubates the eggs.*

Mammals

INTRODUCTION

The mammals are the most advanced of all vertebrates and are the dominant land animals all over the earth. There are a number of features which distinguish mammals from other animals. The most obvious are the possession of hair, and of mammary glands with which the female suckles her young. These features are not shared by any other class of animals. Mammals and birds are the only animals which maintain a constant body temperature. They are aided in this by their fur or feathers. The majority of mammals retain their young in the womb until a fairly late stage of development. Parental care of the young is another important, though not diagnostic, feature of mammalian life. Modern mammals

Order Chiroptera – Bat

have only a single bone in the lower jaw. During their evolution from reptilian ancestors the mammals gradually lost the other bones from the jaw (some are in fact incorporated as the tiny bones of the middle ear).

Fossils indicate that the first mammals appeared in Triassic times, nearly 200 million years ago. These ancient creatures had only one bone in the lower jaw and were thus true mammals. They had by this time probably acquired other mammalian features such as fur and warm blood. The early mammals were about the size of small rats. Their body temperature probably helped them to survive the climatic changes which resulted in the decline of the 'ruling reptiles', e.g. dinosaurs. The mammals then radiated along numerous lines and colonised a wide range of habitats – from the Equator to the Poles.

Kangaroo (order Marsupialia).

Order Tubulidentata
– the Aardvark.

The Hedgehog feeds on insects and worms, etc. (order Insectivora).

Hyrax (order Hyracoidea).

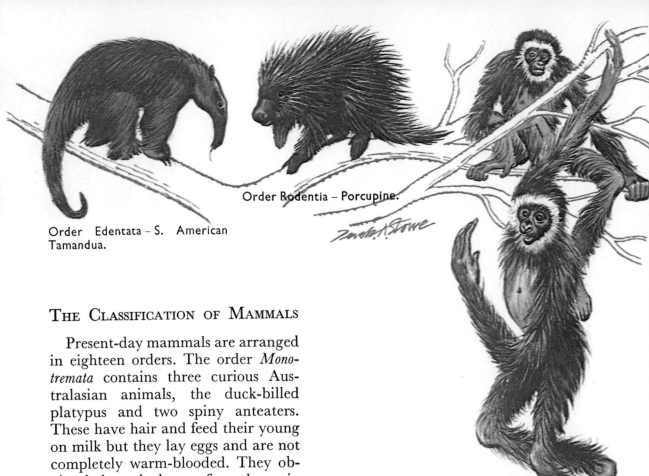

Order Rodentia – Porcupine.

Order Edentata – S. American Tamandua.

The Classification of Mammals

Present-day mammals are arranged in eighteen orders. The order *Monotremata* contains three curious Australasian animals, the duck-billed platypus and two spiny anteaters. These have hair and feed their young on milk but they lay eggs and are not completely warm-blooded. They obviously branched away from the main line very early in mammalian evolution and they are included in a separate sub-class – the Prototheria.

The order *Marsupialia* (the 'pouched mammals') is now confined to Australasia and some parts of America, although at one time the marsupials had a world-wide distribution. They have survived mainly in those isolated regions where there has been no competition with the morc advanced *placental* mammals. The marsupials give birth to their young at an early stage but keep them in a special pouch and feed them on milk for two months or more. In Australia, cut off from the evolving placental mammals, the marsupials have radiated and show remarkable parallels with their placental counterparts in other parts of the world. There are marsupial dogs and mice and even moles and ant-eaters, all of

The Primates, e.g. the Gibbons, have five-fingered limbs and binocular vision to aid them in their arboreal life.

The Monotremes such as this Platypus have hair but lay eggs. They are very primitive mammals.

The rabbit has eyes at the sides of the head giving all-round vision. Carnivores such as the cat have eyes at the front giving binocular vision.

which, because of similar habits, show strong likenesses to their placental equivalents. Kangaroos, koala bears and opossums are all marsupials.

The great majority of mammals are placentals (*i.e.* they retain the young in the womb, nourishing it until birth through a special attachment – the *placenta*). The most primitive living placentals are the shrews, moles and hedgehogs (order *Insectivora*). They have the typical five digits on each limb and they walk on the soles of the feet (*plantigrade* manner).

Bats (order *Chiroptera*) are the only truly flying mammals. Their wings are formed by thin membranes stretched between the fingers and the hind limbs. Bats feed mainly on insects but some of the larger ones eat fruit. The ears are always large – to pick up the high-pitched sounds by which bats find their way in the dark (*echo-location*).

The order *Edentata* contains three South American groups: armadillos, ant-eaters and sloths. Their teeth are reduced or absent, consistent with a diet of soft-bodied invertebrates, especially ants.

Man, monkeys and lemurs are all members of the order *Primates*. They are mainly tree-living and have retained the primitive five-fingered limb which is adaptable for grasping. Development of the eyes and brain are important features of primates. The eyes are placed at the front of the head giving *binocular* vision. The

Whales, sirenians (centre) and seals have all become adapted for life in the sea but seals still go on land to breed.

The zebra (Perissodactyla) and antelopes (Artiodactyla) are camouflaged to protect them from carnivores such as the lion which is itself camouflaged. The elephant has no enemies other than man.

teeth are not highly specialised for the diet is omnivorous.

The *Rodentia* are the commonest mammals – both as individuals and as species. The important factors in their success are their small size and rapid breeding. The incisor teeth (one pair in each jaw) are very sharp and grow continuously to compensate for the continual wear during gnawing. Beavers, rats and mice, guinea-pigs and squirrels are examples of rodents. Rabbits and hares are similar but are grouped in a separate order, the *Lagomorpha*.

Whales (order *Cetacea*) are completely marine. They have reverted to a fish-shape, losing their hind limbs in the process. There are two groups – the *toothed whales* which eat

squids and fishes, and the toothless *whalebone whales* which feed entirely on the minute organisms of the plankton.

The *Carnivora* is a large order containing a number of distinct forms. The sub-order *Fissipeda* contains the wolves and dogs, bears, weasels and badgers and the cat family (*Felidae*). The teeth are normally adapted for tearing flesh. Bears however are more omnivorous and lack the characteristic carnassial teeth. The carnivores frequently have binocular vision and are often camouflaged, *e.g.* the leopard, in order to remain concealed from their prey. They usually walk on their digits (*digitigrade* manner). Seals and walruses, of the sub-order *Pinnipeda*, are also carnivores. Their limbs are flippers and they come on land to breed. Family associations are well developed among the carnivores.

The *Ungulates* are a large group of animals with a number of orders which include the elephants, hyraxes and sea-cows and the hoofed mammals. They are herbivorous and have large grinding teeth. There are two orders of hoofed mammals – the *Perissodactyla* and the *Artiodactyla*. They walk on the tips of the digits (*unguligrade* manner) giving them longer legs and therefore increased speed. The perissodactyls include the horse and rhinoceros. The latter have four digits but in the horses only the middle one is well developed. The artiodactyls – cows, deer and pigs – normally walk on two digits. They are the 'cloven-hoofed' mammals. Many are *ruminants* (*i.e.* they chew the cud), and they are frequently horned. The

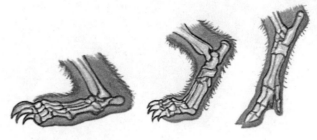

Mammals walk on the soles of their feet (plantigrade), or on all their digits (digitigrade) or on one or two digits (unguligrade).

herding instinct is highly developed in these mammals as a protection against predators and as a regulator of grazing. Camouflage and swift running also help them to escape from enemies.

CHAPTER TWENTY-SEVEN

Feeding and Digestion

MAMMALS feed on a very wide variety of materials, both plant and animal, and the teeth and jaws are wonderfully adapted to the diet of the species.

Teeth

In other vertebrates, the teeth are usually numerous and all of more or less the same shape – simple cones. Their function is more to hold food and prevent its escape than to chew it up. In mammals, however, the teeth are used to chew up the food before it passes to the stomach. Each mammalian species has a fixed number of teeth – in a few there are none – of one or more kinds. At the front of the jaws there are a number of chisel-shaped incisors, used for cutting the food and biting pieces away. Behind them is a stabbing canine or eye tooth – especially well developed in carnivorous mammals.

Then come a number of cheek teeth – the premolars and molars. This is the generalised condition in placental mammals. The detailed structure and arrangement of the teeth depends on diet. Grazing animals such as cattle often have no canine teeth and their cheek teeth have broad, ridged surfaces which grind the food up. Carnivores have sharp-edged cheek teeth which shear through the flesh of their victims.

The number and type of the teeth

Carnivores (left) have sharp cutting teeth in contrast to the heavy grinding teeth of the herbivorous ungulates.

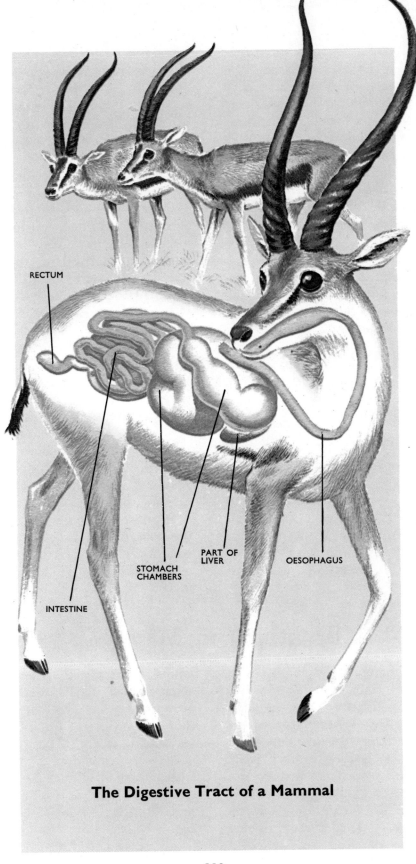

RECTUM

INTESTINE

STOMACH
CHAMBERS

PART OF
LIVER

OESOPHAGUS

The Digestive Tract of a Mammal

of an animal can be expressed simply by means of the *dental formula*. This gives the number of teeth of each type in each half of the upper and lower jaws. The number of incisors is given first, followed by the number of canines, then premolars, then molars. The numbers for the lower jaw are written under the corresponding numbers for the upper jaw. Thus the formula for the generalised placental mammal such as the hedgehog is: $\dfrac{3143}{3143}$, making a total of 44 teeth (the formula gives the number in only one half of each jaw). But few mammals retain the full set of 44 teeth. Man's dental formula is: $\dfrac{2123}{2123}$ and that for the rabbit, which has no canine teeth, is $\dfrac{2033}{1023}$.

Digestion

Salivary glands are well developed in mammals and the food is well chewed and wetted in the mouth. In primates and some other mammals the starch-splitting enzyme ptyalin is found in the saliva and digestion starts in the mouth. The rest of the aliment-ary canal in carnivorous and omnivorous mammals is very much as described in an earlier chapter but the ungulate (hoofed) mammals and other herbivores are interesting in that parts of the gut are specialised as chambers in which the cellulose of plant food can be broken down by the activities of bacteria. In the odd-toed ungulates (horses, etc.) the caecum is modified, but in even-toed ungulates (cows) the stomach is modified. In the cow, for example, the stomach is a large four-chambered organ. Food is eaten and swallowed. It passes down the oesophagus to the first chamber of the stomach. From time to time it is brought up and chewed – a process that is commonly termed 'chewing the cud'. It is then swallowed again, whence it passes into the other chambers in turn where it is acted upon by bacteria.

Very few animals produce an enzyme that is able to break down cellulose, and must rely on the activities of bacteria.

In most mammals the rectum and the excretory ducts do not open into a common cloaca. Each system has a separate opening.

CHAPTER TWENTY-EIGHT

Breathing in Mammals

THE mammalian lungs are extremely complicated organs. As in all tetrapods, they open into the throat by way of the trachea or windpipe. This divides into two bronchi – one leading to each lung. The bronchi each divide further into smaller tubes called bronchioles which, after further division, end up in tiny pockets called alveoli. There are millions of these tiny pockets, joined by connective tissues into a spongy mass. The walls of the alveoli are only one cell thick and it is here that oxygen passes from the air into the blood stream. The vast number of alveoli means that there is a great surface area for diffusion – it has been calculated that the surface area of a man's lungs is equal to about half a tennis court.

Air is drawn into the lungs by

suction. Mammals possess a diaphragm – a muscular sheet of tissue
stretching across the body cavity and
separating the chest or thoracic cavity
from the abdomen which contains the
digestive organs. During inspiration
the muscles of the diaphragm pull it
downwards. Muscles attached to the
ribs pull them outwards and so the
chest cavity is enlarged. Air then
rushes into the lungs to counteract
the reduced pressure in the surrounding cavity. At expiration these
muscles relax and another set contract
and force air out of the lungs. Elastic
fibres in the lung alveoli also contract
and force air out.

During breathing, only a very small
amount of the air in the lungs is
actually exchanged. The intricate
divisions of the bronchioles and alveoli are such that much of the air
in them cannot escape. Oxygen from
the freshly inspired air has to diffuse
through this accumulated stale air
before it reaches the actual respiratory surface of the alveoli. Seals are
able to exchange about 70% of the
air in their lungs at each breath – far

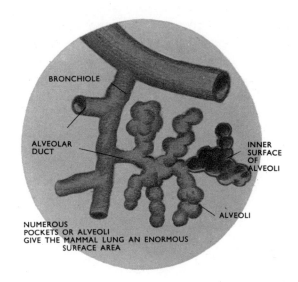

more than most other mammals.
They therefore obtain far more
oxygen at each breath – a fact that
helps them to stay under water for
long periods. They are also less
sensitive than most mammals to the
accumulation of waste carbon dioxide
in the blood. It is this waste carbon
dioxide in the blood that acts on
the breathing centres of the vertebrate
brain and thus controls the breathing
rate.

CHAPTER TWENTY-NINE

The Nervous System

THE mammalian brain is completely dominated by the cerebral
hemispheres. The roof has developed
enormously and spread out forming
the *cerebral cortex* which in man is
thrown into a number of elaborate
folds and almost covers the rest of the
brain. The cortex is made up of millions of cells. The more folded the
surface, the more cells it can contain.
These cells make up the 'grey matter'.
Their axons, which make up the *tracts*

or pathways in the brain, form the
'*white matter*' underneath the cortex.
The '*white matter*' of the spinal cord is
also made up of nerve axons, surrounding the central '*grey matter*'.

Most of the nervous functions in
the mammal are taken over by the
cerebral cortex. The cerebellum remains large and active, however, and
the thalamus is enlarged for that is
where the nerves of the sensory and
motor systems link up and pass to and

from the cortex where the messages are 'sorted out', 'stored' (i.e. remembered) and acted upon when necessary. The behaviour, both learned and instinctive of mammals, is controlled by the cortex. Each region of the latter controls certain aspects of behaviour such as sight, memory, speech in man, etc. Removal of any part of the cortex may produce definite changes in character or behaviour.

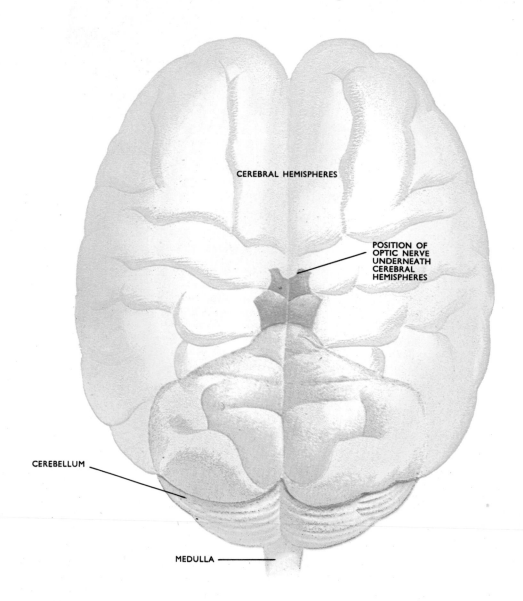

CEREBRAL HEMISPHERES

POSITION OF OPTIC NERVE UNDERNEATH CEREBRAL HEMISPHERES

CEREBELLUM

MEDULLA

The brain of man is viewed from above and slightly from behind. This, together with the ghosting of parts underneath the cerebral hemispheres, shows the positions and proportions of the fore-, mid-, and hind-brains.

CHAPTER THIRTY

Reproduction in Mammals

REPRODUCTION in mammals is on three distinct levels, represented by the egg-laying monotremes, the pouched marsupials, and the placentals – whose young are nourished within the mother's body by a special organ called the placenta.

MAMMALS THAT LAY EGGS

The egg-laying monotremes diverged from the main line of mammalian evolution at a very early stage and they have remained at this stage ever since – still showing many features indicating a close relationship with the reptiles. These egg-laying mammals are confined to the Australasian region. They are the duck-billed platypus and the echidnas or spiny ant-eaters.

The female Platypus builds a nest of damp leaves and grasses in which she usually lays two eggs.

Though its egg-laying habits are primitive, the Duck-billed Platypus (Ornithorhynchus) is highly adapted for spending much of its time in water.

Their affinities with the reptiles are especially obvious through similarities in the bones of the skull, the backbone, and the limbs and limb girdles. The gut, reproductive and excretory systems open into a common chamber, the *cloaca*, and, perhaps the most striking characteristic of all, they lay large, yolky eggs that have shells. The young escape from the eggs by means of a special egg-tooth and another structure, the caruncle, at the end of the bill. They are suckled by the female, however, and feed on milk produced by specialised sweat glands on the abdomen. These open as slits; the ducts do not form nipples as in other mammals.

The Platypus builds an elaborate system of narrow underground tunnels for nesting. These are up to a foot below the surface and may be twenty yards long. The main tunnel leading to the nesting chamber winds about and it has barriers of soft earth placed along it at regular intervals by the female. She does this with her flattened tail, which is also a useful swimming organ. The female builds the nest itself of damp leaves and grasses.

Platypuses pair in the water, the time of the year during which it occurs varying from one part of Australia to another (between July and August).

The right ovary does not function, as in birds. The eggs, dirty white in colour and usually two in number, are laid about a fortnight after pairing. They are just under an inch in diameter. The female incubates the eggs by holding them on her abdomen.

Young platypuses are born naked and blind. They stay in the nest for four or five months while they are nourished on milk produced by the mother. They are not fed for the first week after they hatch. The milk is yellow in colour and is very rich and creamy. Since the milk glands have no nipples, the female lies on her back and allows the milk to trickle out onto

Apart from the Platypus, the Australian Echidna (Tachyglossus) *and the long-beaked Echidna* (Zaglossus) (*right*) *are the only mammals that lay eggs.*

her abdomen over two patches of tissue.

The female Echidna grows a pouch during the breeding season. She lays only one egg and, with her beak-like muzzle places it in the pouch to incubate it. The youngster hatches in the pouch and feeds there on milk. After a period of weaning, the young are left to fend for themselves.

Parental care amongst monotremes has reached a higher level than that found in reptiles, therefore. The eggs are incubated, and the young are fed and cared for after they have hatched.

THE POUCHED MAMMALS

The pouched mammals, or *marsupials*, differ from the highest group of mammals (*placentals*) in a striking way. The young are born at a very early stage in their development – in the Opossum from only eight to thirteen days after fertilization has occurred. They then crawl to a pouch on the abdomen of the female where they spend the early part of their lives, being suckled on milk from the mammary glands.

The Kangaroo is probably the best known Marsupial. Others include the Wombat, Koala, Native Cat, Tasmanian Devil, Wallaby and the Banded Ant-Eater.

Not all marsupials have a pouch or *marsupium* as well-developed as that of the Kangaroo. Some merely have two flaps of skin whilst others, for example the Woolly Opossum, have no pouch. In this case the youngsters hang on to the nipples of the female as she moves around.

In the placental mammals (e.g. Rabbit) the developing embryo obtains its nourishment from the mother

A Koala carrying a youngster on her back.

by way of a *placenta* – a specialised organ formed by the union of the womb lining and certain embryonic tissues. Such a device permits a long period of development and consequently the young are well developed at birth. In marsupials, however, the young are not nourished by a placenta, except in the Bandicoot, but even here the placenta is relatively simple in structure. As embryos, the only nourishment they have is the store of yolky material in the egg and a supply of 'milk' from the womb (*uterus*) lining. The yolk is quickly exhausted and consequently the young are born at an immature stage. They have to reach the pouch where, clinging to the nipples with their mouths, they can obtain the nourishment required for their further development.

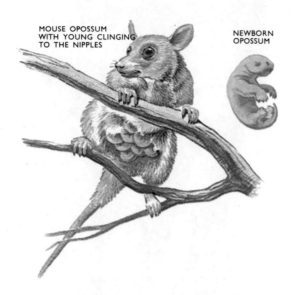

MOUSE OPOSSUM
WITH YOUNG CLINGING
TO THE NIPPLES

NEWBORN
OPOSSUM

At birth, the offspring of the Virginia Opossum are no larger than a honey bee. Even those of the Great Grey Kangaroo are merely an inch or so long and weigh only an ounce.

The female does not pick up the newborn youngsters and place them in her pouch. They find their own way there, a quite remarkable feat for such immature creatures. Associated with this, the forelimbs and their nervous supply are well developed at birth. The hind limbs are relatively undeveloped at this stage. The mother may lick the fur on her abdomen to assist the youngsters' journey to the pouch.

The length of time that the young spend in the pouch varies from about seven weeks in the Marsupial Cat to four months in the Rat Kangaroo. Young of the Virginia Opossum are nursed for nearly two months and they do not become independent of the mother for at least three months.

Generally, a large number of young are produced. Ten is an average litter for the Virginia Opossum, though ones of fifteen to eighteen are not uncommon, but the Rat Kangaroo produces only one. This is a curious situation, for the latter has four teats, – three are usually unoccupied therefore – whilst the Opossum has thirteen teats

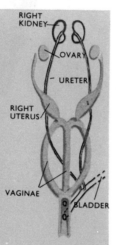

The reproductive system of a female Wallaby. Note that the two oviducts, even their lower uterine segments, remain separate along their length including paired vaginae. The middle vagina acquires an opening into the chamber below during pregnancy and this may be permanent. In the male the testes are enclosed in a sac or scrotum.

RIGHT KIDNEY
OVARY
URETER
RIGHT UTERUS
VAGINAE
BLADDER

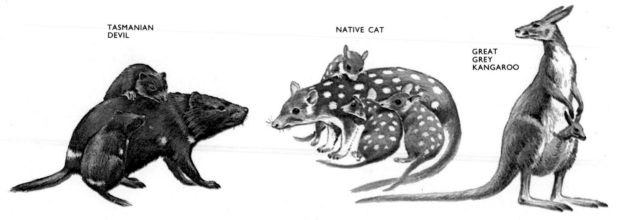

TASMANIAN DEVIL

NATIVE CAT

GREAT GREY KANGAROO

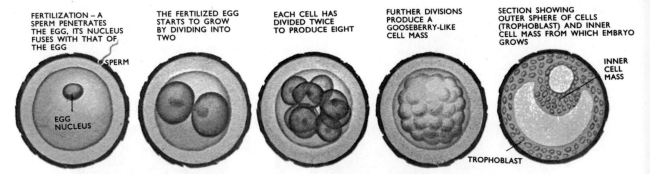

FERTILIZATION – A SPERM PENETRATES THE EGG, ITS NUCLEUS FUSES WITH THAT OF THE EGG

SPERM

EGG NUCLEUS

THE FERTILIZED EGG STARTS TO GROW BY DIVIDING INTO TWO

EACH CELL HAS DIVIDED TWICE TO PRODUCE EIGHT

FURTHER DIVISIONS PRODUCE A GOOSEBERRY-LIKE CELL MASS

SECTION SHOWING OUTER SPHERE OF CELLS (TROPHOBLAST) AND INNER CELL MASS FROM WHICH EMBRYO GROWS

INNER CELL MASS

TROPHOBLAST

Several Stages in the Early Development of the Pig.

(eleven that actually produce milk), which means that in litters of twelve or more, surplus young die because they are unable to obtain nourishment.

From a study of marsupials, both in the wild and in captivity, it seems that they are able to breed at any time of the year, though strict breeding seasons are normally observed. A Virginia Opossum female usually has two litters a year and becomes pregnant again after the first litter has been weaned.

THE PLACENTAL MAMMALS

The Platypus and the Echidnas are mammals that lay eggs. The young hatch as very immature individuals entirely dependent on their mother for some time after birth. Young platypuses are unable to see for the first eleven weeks of their life. The pouched mammals (e.g. Kangaroos) do not lay eggs, but they give birth to very undeveloped young after they have spent an extremely short period of development within the mother. The young continue their development clinging to the nipples of the mother inside a pouch. The young of placental mammals, however, have a long period of development within the

FEATURES OF EMBRYO BEGINNING TO APPEAR – HEAD, TAIL ETC., PLACENTA WELL FORMED

HEAD AND TAIL STILL MORE OBVIOUS AND MANY INTERNAL STRUCTURES BEGINNING TO APPEAR

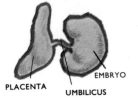

PLACENTA

EMBRYO

UMBILICUS

SUCH FEATURES AS EYES, LIMBS AND TAIL BECOMING MORE OBVIOUS

PIG-LIKE SNOUT NOW OBVIOUS, EARS BECOMING MORE VISIBLE

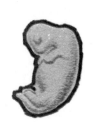

EMBRYO OF ABOUT SIX WEEKS

TOES, ETC. NOW CLEAR

Red deer stags fight amongst themselves for the hinds during the autumn. The stags have antlers but the females (inset) lack them.

mother. This is permitted by means of an elaborate organ, the *placenta*. It allows extremely close contact between the blood vessels of the mother and those of the growing embryos so that adequate supplies of food (e.g. sugar molecules) are continually carried to them. Within the mother they are also protected. Placentals have an almost constant body temperature, maintained above that of the surroundings. An embryo enclosed in this way within remarkably constant surroundings for a long period of time, can reach a high degree of development (though not all placentals are well developed at birth and a considerable period of maternal care is often necessary). A placenta is one of several important factors that allow the great development of the nervous system associated with placental mammals, and so their whole behaviour patterns are more complicated. A young Giraffe can run almost as fast as its parents soon after its birth: a young Zebra can leap in the air. A newly born Opossum, on the other hand, is able merely to make the journey to the pouch. For this purpose,

only the forelimbs and associated nerves are well developed.

The *placenta* is formed from the lining of the mother's uterus and certain of the embryonic tissues – the *allantois*. For this reason it is known as an *allantoic placenta*. The placenta is rich in blood vessels, partly supplied by the mother and partly by the embryo or *foetus*. Food materials and oxygen pass from the blood vessels of the mother into those of the foetus, and waste substances (e.g. urea and carbon dioxide) in the reverse direction. The placenta persists throughout the development of the young.

The length of time that the young are carried by the mother varies from three weeks in House mice to twenty-two months in Elephants.

Courtship and display in mammals is rarely as spectacular as that found in birds. Nevertheless, elaborate signalling methods exist for bringing the sexes together. In most mammals the sense of smell is of great importance in this respect, particularly in the initial stages. For example, the urine of a female Red Squirrel excites the male, and a female Sable in heat leaves an oily trail on surrounding objects. In some species there are noticeable differences between the sexes other than in the reproductive system. These are known as *secondary sexual characters*. Thus a male Lion is maned and a male Red Deer has antlers. Some mammals, especially primates (Man, Apes, Monkeys, etc.) make particular use of facial expressions.

The majority of female placentals will pair only at certain times of the year. Each of these is referred to as *'oestrus'* or 'heat'. Oestrus is preceded by a preparatory phase called *proestrus*. The beginning of this period marks the onset of the sexual season. Eggs begin to develop in the ovaries and there are other marked changes in the reproductive organs. Activities of the endocrine system 'prepare' the nervous system of an individual so that it reacts in the correct way to stimulation by indi-

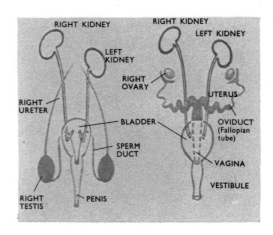

The reproductive system of (left) a male and (right) a female rabbit. Note that uterus is double (single in man).

viduals of the opposite sex during oestrus.

The whole variety of internal and external changes is designed to bring male and female together at the right time – the chances of fertilization are high, therefore. To ensure that the

The young of a rabbit are very undeveloped at birth. They are suckled on milk supplied by the mammary gland of the mother.

fertilized egg is protected and nourished from the start, the uterus is fully prepared to receive it. If an egg is fertilized successfully, and is retained within the body of the female, *gestation* follows. This is the period during which the young are nourished and protected within the mother. Gestation is followed by nursing or *lactation* – the suckling phase during which the young feed on the mother's milk. A resting, non-breeding phase (*anoestrus*) may follow lactation. In the rat the birth of the young is followed by another proestrus and oestrus during lactation. Alternatively, lactation may be followed almost immediately by another period of 'heat'.

If fertilization does not occur, oestrus is followed by a brief recovery period – *metoestrus*. Then the changes that occurred during proestrus and oestrus slowly subside. Alternatively changes occur similar to those that take place during pregnancy. The *pseudopregnant* period is longer than metoestrus. Pseudopregnancy is then succeeded by another oestrus or in

some instances anoestrus. The changes described above constitute the *oestrous cycle*. If fertilization occurs it will be interrupted by the gestation period. In many primates, including Man, the thickened lining of the uterus, built up during pseudopregnancy, sloughs off together with some loss of blood, a process called *menstruation*.

There is considerable variation in the length of the oestrous cycle in different species. In the White Rat it is as short as five days, but in the Chimpanzee takes five weeks. Some species (e.g. Bears) have only one oestrous cycle per year. They are said to be *monoestrous. Polyoestrous* species (e.g. most primates) have several cycles in the course of a year. Occasionally climatic conditions will affect an animals' physiology so that while it has a definite breeding season over part of its range, it will breed all the year round over the remainder.

The act of pairing usually takes place on land, but whales and their relatives, the Muskrat, the European Otter and certain seals, pair in water.

CHAPTER THIRTY-ONE

The Biology of Milk

MILK is the fluid produced by the mammary glands, after the birth of the young. It is a fluid characteristic of mammals; these are the only animals to suckle their young. Milk is an extremely rich source of protein food and milk from various mammals is an important dietary item all over the world.

Commercially, cattle are by far the most important producers of milk and references to milk apply to cattle, unless otherwise qualified. The metabolism of a dairy cow is 'geared' to producing milk which is why her build is much slighter than that of a cow reared for beef.

Milk is composed principally of water – around 87 per cent – and also contains proteins, milk sugar or lactose, most vitamins – even though the quantities of some are negligible traces – fat and various salts. It is particularly rich in calcium, which is of obvious importance to the growing young animal whose sole source of food initially is milk. Calcium is required in large quantities for bone formation. The amount of calcium in human milk is, not surprisingly, much lower than that in cow's milk. The demands of a growing calf are way beyond those of a much slower growing and smaller human youngster. The percentage of protein in cow's milk is correspondingly higher.

Milk is a type of colloid known as an emulsion (a 3-4% emulsion of fat stabilized by milk protein), that is, physically it consists of a liquid dispersed within a liquid. Its ivory coloration is a result of the almost equal scattering of all wavelengths of light. The slightly yellow tint of the cream is due to the pigment *carotene* (this is the precursor of vitamin A – important in vision – which is formed in the liver). A layer of cream forms on top of the more watery remainder because the larger fat droplets float to the surface. Milk is usually slightly acid, having a pH of between 6·6 and 6·8.

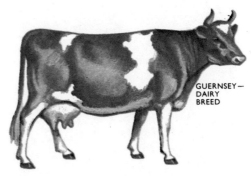

GUERNSEY – DAIRY BREED

Illustrations showing the characteristic builds of dairy cattle (above) and beef cattle (below). The latter have a much heavier build and the chest is especially deep – metabolism is diverted towards flesh production. The lighter built dairy beast is primarily a milk producer whose metabolism is 'geared' in this direction.

ABERDEEN ANGUS-BEEF BREED

Diagrams showing the major constituents of cows' milk and human milk. The principal constituent is water. Note that the percentage of protein in cows' milk is higher than in human milk as is the salt proportion, the latter being largely due to the large quantities of calcium present. The growth rate of a calf is much greater than that of a child, hence the greater requirement for protein (muscles) and calcium (bones).

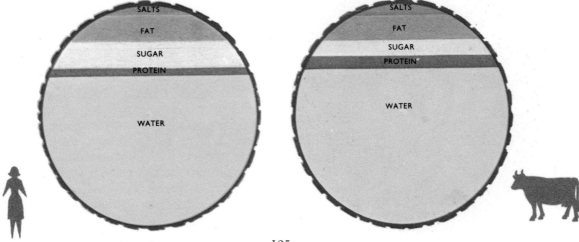

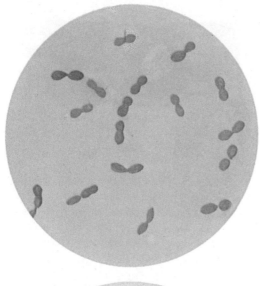

The main protein of milk is *casein* (or caseinogen). About three and a half per cent of milk is protein: two thirds of this is casein. The enzyme, *rennin*, acts on casein causing it to clot. It is especially active in young mammals whose sole diet consists of milk. Analysis of the casein molecules shows it to contain all the essential amino acids that the body is unable to make itself.

The only sugar present in milk is *lactose*. It is found in the milk of all mammals and is formed in the mammary gland and no other part of the body. Lactose is a *disaccharide*, its molecule being composed of one molecule of glucose and one molecule of galactose. Just under five per cent of lactose is usually present in cow's milk, but human milk contains up to seven per cent and a cow elephant as much as seven and a half per cent. In a doe rabbit only two per cent lactose is found. Thus the composition and quality of the milk of different species of mammals varies considerably. It is interesting that in whales there is 12 times more milk-fat and four times more protein than there is in cow's milk. Fat is of great importance as a heat insulatory material to aquatic mammals and also as an energy store for their long migrations from polar seas to more temperate waters.

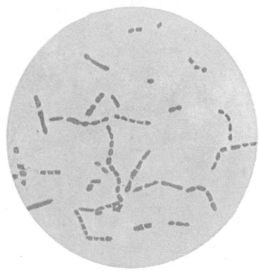

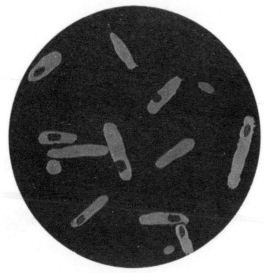

Some of the bacteria that occur in milk or milk products. From top to bottom. Streptococcus lactis *an organism that causes milk to sour by producing lactic acid.* Streptococcus thermophilus *and* Lactobacillus bulgaricus *used in the making of yoghourt and* Clostridium tyrobutyricum *an anaerobic bacterium causing blowing of hard cheeses.*

Souring of milk is due to the fermenting activities of *Streptococcus lactis* and many other organisms infecting it. Enzymes that these micro-organisms contain convert lactose into lactic acid. The increase in acidity precipitates the protein in milk producing the characteristic curdling.

The principal site of fat synthesis in the vertebrate body is the liver. But, in mammals, the mammary glands are important sites of fat production outside the liver. Much of the body fat is composed of long chain fatty acids but milk fats contain considerably more short chain fatty acids such as butyric acid and caproic acid. This is probably related to the great production of organic acids in the rumen (a chamber of the stomach) from the cellulose of plant material by the actions of micro-organisms. There is much less butyric acid and caproic acid in human milk where bacterial action in the gut takes place on a much smaller scale.

The principal fats are triglycerides such as tripalmitin, tristearin, and triolein. In addition, milk contains lipids such as lecithin and cholesterol. The latter is related chemically to the bile salts and the sex hormones.

The main salts present in milk are the chlorides and phosphates of calcium, sodium and potassium. Calcium and phosphorus are particularly necessary for teeth and bone formation. Each litre of milk contains 1,200 milligrams of calcium (cheese, incidentally, contains nearly that amount in each 100 grams). Vitamins C and D are present in negligible quantities (this is why dried milk, and the products used for feeding infants have vitamins added to them as an anti-ricketic), and only riboflavin of the vitamin B complex, but all other vitamins are present with especially large quantities of riboflavin and pantothenic acid. Human milk contains more ascorbic acid.

The Formation of Milk

The udder of a cow has a rich blood supply and prominent milk veins can be seen on the abdomen of a dairy cow. It might be expected that the milk-producing cells of the udder merely filter substances from the blood, thus making milk. But this is only partly the case. Certainly blood contains sugars, fats, proteins, vitamins, salts and all the other ingredients of milk. However, the sugar in the blood is glucose: that of milk is lactose. Obviously, therefore, chemical changes occur in the udder during the formation of milk, and although the complete chemistry of its formation is far from being known, the little that we do know confirms the existence of a delicate, yet elaborate, metabolic mechanism.

Most of our knowledge has been derived from the use of isotopic tracers. For example, labelling of glucose with carbon-14 – a radioactive isotope of carbon – has shown conclusively that milk sugar (lactose) is formed from glucose derived from the blood. Firstly, glucose is converted into galactose and then a molecule of this is combined with a molecule of glucose to give lactose. The precise sequence of controlled enzyme reactions by which this occurs is not established with certainty, but it is definitely more than a two-stage process as described here, and is probably by step-by-step conversions of organic phosphate intermediates.

Similar experiments 'labelling' fat in the blood have shown that some of the milk fat is derived from blood fat without chemical change. The most important source of fatty acids is probably acetic acid formed in the rumen by the breakdown of cellulose by micro-organisms. Each acetic acid molecule contains two carbon atoms. By means of enzymes these two carbon units are linked together forming chains containing as many as sixteen atoms of carbon. Palmitic acid has sixteen carbon atoms in its molecule. But fatty acid molecules containing eighteen or more carbon atoms, (e.g. stearic acid), are almost certainly obtained 'ready-made' from the blood.

The paths of protein synthesis are not known. It is fairly certain that proteins from the blood are not used to make caesinogen. Its molecule is built up from the 'free' amino acids in the blood flowing through the mammary glands.

The Control of Milk Secretion

There appears to be no actual control of the mammary gland by another distant part of the body as far as milk quality is concerned.

The actual quality of milk produced depends to a certain extent on the cow's diet, though the latter can vary enormously without effect. A general deficiency of food lowers the volume of milk produced but not the quality since the cow's reserves are drawn upon to make up for dietary deficiencies. An example of this is the drain on calcium reserves. A diet continuously low in calcium results in a great loss of calcium from the bones, in acute cases, even producing skeletal abnormalities which may interfere with the calf-bearing abilities of the cow. The butter fat content of milk may vary, however, with the diet. A cow fed on young grass or on a diet low in roughage but high in concentrates may show a butter fat depreciation of more than fifty per cent. This is largely

due to the fact that microbial activity is much reduced in the rumen since the bacteria have less material to ferment and the fatty acids released during cellulose breakdown are important sources of butterfat.

When a cow is milked there is a delay of about half a minute before 'let down' – the time when the milk begins to flow freely. Prior to 'let down' there is a build up in the pressure in the ducts of the mammary gland. This is due to the action of the hormone *oxytocin* on the muscle cells surrounding the ducts and alveoli of the gland. Oxytocin is produced by the hind part of the pituitary gland, in response to massage because of the resulting nervous reflex. It is carried in the blood to the mammary gland

Injection of labelled acetic acid into goats resulted in short chain fatty acid being built up from the 2-c acetic acid units. Labelled fatty acids were later isolated from the milk.

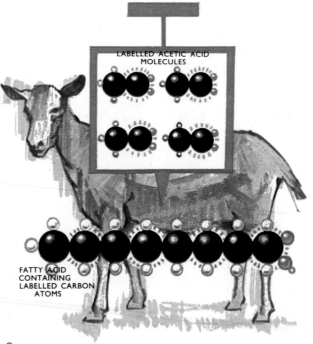

LABELLED ACETIC ACID MOLECULES

FATTY ACID CONTAINING LABELLED CARBON ATOMS

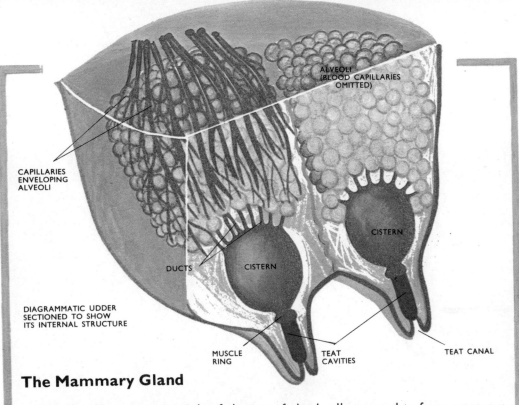

CAPILLARIES ENVELOPING ALVEOLI

ALVEOLI (BLOOD CAPILLARIES OMITTED)

CISTERN

DUCTS CISTERN

DIAGRAMMATIC UDDER SECTIONED TO SHOW ITS INTERNAL STRUCTURE

MUSCLE RING TEAT CAVITIES TEAT CANAL

The Mammary Gland

A cow's udder consists mainly of clusters of gland cells grouped to form numerous tiny, hollow sacs or *alveoli*. Each alveolus is surrounded by blood capillaries from which the gland cells obtain their nourishment and the substances that they convert into milk. In the lactating animal milk is poured continuously into the hollow centre of each alveolus and leaves by a duct. The ducts of the many alveoli join like the tributaries of a river and empty their contents into the storage chamber or *cistern* above each teat. It is thought that the mammary glands may be modified sweat glands because of certain similarities in structure.

where it causes the muscle cells to contract – ultimately with the ejection of milk through the teats. (The same hormone causes the musculature of the uterus to contract during the birth of a calf – and a human child).

The actual formation of milk is probably initiated by another hormone, *prolactin*, produced by the anterior lobe of the pituitary gland. The quantity of milk produced depends to a large extent on the suckling action of a calf or the equivalent action of milking. Frequent and complete milking is thus an important part of dairy cattle management. Suckling and mechanical milking, through nerve reflexes, seem to cause increased pro-

duction of prolactin which therefore stimulates the milk producing cells to greater activity.

The development of the mammary gland in the young cow and the proliferation of its tissues during pregnancy are controlled by a host of hormones – principally sex hormones such as oestrogen and progesterone. Their action in fact prepares the mammary gland for the action of prolactin. A cow does not produce milk until it has had a calf, and in order to obtain as much milk as possible from a cow during its lifetime it is desirable for it to have several calves and thus several periods of lactation.

An Indian elephant at work. These animals have immense strength and are invaluable for moving timber in rough country. African elephants can also be trained to work but are less commonly trained than their Indian cousins.

Some Mammals
of Interest

CHAPTER THIRTY-TWO

Whales

NO ONE can fail to be impressed by the great size of some whales (they include the largest animals ever known on Earth), but more striking than size alone are the features of their anatomy and physiology which make them so wonderfully adapted to lead their entire life in water. Perhaps the most obvious of these is their fish-like appearance – the head is long and, though there are seven neck vertebrae as in other mammals, there is no distinct neck externally between the head and the streamlined body. The forelimbs are modified as paddles and the tail terminates in large, forked, horizontal expansions called the *flukes*. Some species have a fin on their back but this has no skeleton, and the skeleton of the forelimbs is quite unlike that of a fish's paired fins. The hind limbs have been lost in all whales and a pair of small bones is all that remains internally of the hip girdle.

The tail fin of a fish is vertical and moved from side to side to drive the fish forward, but the whale is thrust forward by the vertical movement of the horizontal tail flukes. This structure and the dorsal fin are tough folds of skin.

Like all other mammals, whales are warm-blooded. They breathe air by means of lungs, and suckle their young, which are born alive. The skin, however, is smooth and hairless, except for a few bristles round the mouth in some species. The lack of hair undoubtedly helps to keep the amount of friction to a minimum as the animal moves through the water. The loss of body heat is probably reduced by the *blubber* – the thick layer of fatty tissue beneath the skin – which acts as an insulator. Blubber also increases the whale's buoyancy, and the fat, besides being a food store, is a likely source of water when it is burned to provide energy. Since whales breathe air they must come to the surface periodically to obtain fresh supplies. A characteristic sign of this is the 'blow' which is now thought to consist of exhaled air in which are suspended fine droplets of oil. It is not due merely to the hot breath condensing in the colder air, for the 'blow' is visible in the tropics as well as in polar regions. It has a characteristic fetid smell.

The skeleton of a whalebone whale. Note the great length of the head, modified forelimbs and the absence of hind-limbs.

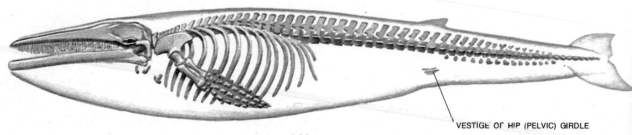

VESTIGE OF HIP (PELVIC) GIRDLE

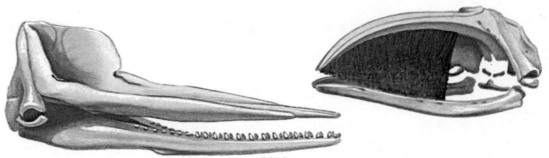

The nostrils open on top of the head, an adaptation which means that a whale needs only to raise the top of its head out of the water to obtain air. The upper end of the trachea forms a tube that fits into the nose chamber in the skull. The windpipe and the lungs are thus cut off from the mouth and this can be opened under water without water passing into the lungs. The nostrils can be closed by powerful muscles during dives so that the whale can hold its breath while beneath the surface. Dives of an hour's duration have been recorded.

The lungs are filled mainly by the action of the chest muscles. As in other water-dwelling mammals the diaphragm is less important. Air is taken in rapidly as soon as the whale breaks the surface. In various parts of the body there are elaborate networks of blood vessels – the *retia mirabilia*. Besides the oxygen taken into the lungs an extra supply is

The skulls of a toothed whale (left) and a whalebone whale, showing the many similar teeth of the former and the absence of teeth in the latter which has a row of baleen plates on each side (one shown) of the upper jaw.

available during dives from the store in these vessels. The muscles, too, store large amounts of oxygen, and the rate at which they work is lowered during dives so that less oxygen is consumed. A human diver is continually supplied with air under pressure and, consequently, if he surfaces too rapidly the additional quantities of nitrogen that have dissolved in the blood escape as bubbles and cause Caisson sickness or 'bends'. But the whale takes down a large supply of air with it. The great pressure collapses the lungs and forces the air in them out into spaces within the whale. It is believed that a fatty emulsion absorbs any nitrogen present in this air and so the quantity in the blood does not increase. When the

A dissection of a porpoise, showing how the elongated upper end of the windpipe fits into the nose chamber, thus forming a continuous closed airway between the blowhole and the lungs.

BLOWHOLE

BRAIN

PART OF 'RETIA'

TRACHEA (WINDPIPE)

LEFT LUNG

whale surfaces the fatty droplets are expelled in the blow. Thus a whale does not suffer from Caisson sickness.

Hearing is the main sense of whales, vision and smell are less acute. The brain is very large (much larger than our own) and they are very intelligent. Many whales make elaborate noises – and these seem to be a form of speech by which they communicate with each other.

There are two main groups of whales: the toothed whales or *Odontoceti*, and the whalebone whales or *Mysticeti*. The Odontocetes form the largest group and include the sperm whale, bottle-nosed whale, narwhal, white whale, pilot whale or blackfish, killer whale and the dolphins and porpoises.

The sperm whale is the largest of them, reaching a length of sixty feet and weighing as much as fifty tons. It lives mainly in warm water. Its head is an enormous blunt-ended structure, the snout of which forms a reservoir of oil or *spermaceti*. Sperm whales probably dive deeper than other whales and it may be that this oil is able to absorb the greater quantities of nitrogen released from the lungs. The lower jaw is small by comparison. Sperm whales feed principally on squids. These are mainly about three feet long, but giant specimens over thirty feet long have been found in the stomachs of captured sperm whales. Sperm whales have been recovered from considerable depths caught up in submarine cables. Hence it is suggested that they often search along the sea floor scooping up their prey with the lower jaw. The killer whale, or grampus, is the fiercest of whales. It moves about in groups or schools feeding principally on seals and porpoises – though several will make vicious attacks on another (much larger) whale. Many captured sperm whales have been found badly wounded, with one or both of the front paddles and other parts of the body torn off – vivid examples of the ferocity of killer whales.

The porpoises and dolphins often travel in schools. The common porpoise reaches a length of about five feet and the common dolphin is generally larger, some attaining a length of about eight feet. They feed mainly on fishes.

The Mysticeti or whalebone whales possess teeth only when they are very young. These are absorbed and in the upper jaw the long horny plates of *baleen* are developed. They are used to strain plankton from the water. The whales move along with the mouth open. It is then closed, the tongue and floor of the mouth are raised and water is forced out through the sides of the mouth, leaving the tiny planktonic organisms behind on the baleen.

The blue whale is the largest animal ever known to inhabit the Earth. It may reach one hundred feet in length and weigh upwards of one hundred and twenty tons. Blue whales feed principally on tiny shrimp-like creatures called euphausids – known as *krill*. Smaller planktonic organisms pass through the straining apparatus.

Other whalebone whales include the humpback whale, fin whale, sei whale and lesser rorqual. These are collectively termed *rorquals*. Another group of whalebone whales are the *right whales*, so named because they were recognised by whale fishermen as being easier to catch and of greater value.

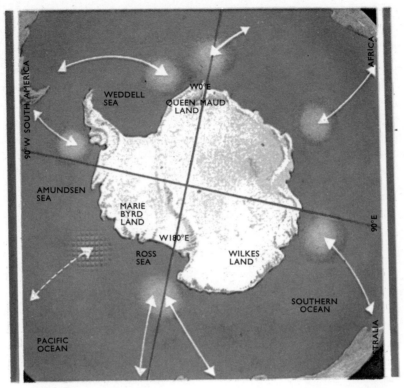

A map of Antarctica showing the migration of humpback whales. Marking experiments indicate that they keep to well-defined groups as shown.

Little was known until recently of the age that whales attain. Certain structures (corpora lutea) present in the ovaries were used to estimate the age of captured female whales, but now a new method has been discovered. In the ear passage of whales a solid mass of wax forms. It is built up by the addition of small amounts of wax annually. The number of layers therefore gives an accurate estimate of a whale's age.

Whales are slow-breeding animals and they have been overfished to such an extent that several species are now extinct and others face probable extinction.

Many whales migrate from the polar regions towards the equator at the end of the polar summer during which they have built up a large reserve of body fat through feeding

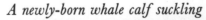

A newly-born whale calf suckling

on the rich supply of plankton. It is during these migrations that the young are born. Pregnancy lasts for about a year in the blue whale, fin whale and humpback whale. Normally only one youngster is born at a time. A young blue whale is about twenty-four feet long at birth (the humpback sixteen feet) and the period of suckling is about seven months. In this time a blue whale has reached a length of fifty feet! The mammary glands (of which there are a pair) are each provided with a powerful muscle which pumps milk into the youngster's mouth when it touches or grasps the teat.

A blue whale is able to breed when it is two years old and it is then about eighty-five feet long.

CHAPTER THIRTY-THREE

Elephants

THE first elephants to walk the Earth lived in Eocene times some sixty million years ago. The earliest known fossils – discovered in Egypt – are of a creature called *Moeritherium*. In general appearance this creature was nothing like a modern elephant. It was only about two feet high and had no trunk. However, the structure of the skull and the form of the teeth show that it was a very primitive kind of elephant. From ancestors similar to this, arose the whole range of living and extinct elephants – a total of about three hundred and fifty species.

Elephants Today

Out of the vast number of elephants and near-elephants that have existed, only two species are alive today. These are the African Elephant (*Loxodonta africana*) and the Indian or Asiatic Elephant (*Elephas maximus*), which

Two of the rather strange elephants of Miocene times. Left is a typical dinothere head. It lacked tusks in the upper jaw and those of the lower jaw curved backwards. Right is one of the 'shovel-tuskers' – so called because of the large lower jaw. They probably lived in swamps and shovelled up vegetation with their jaws.

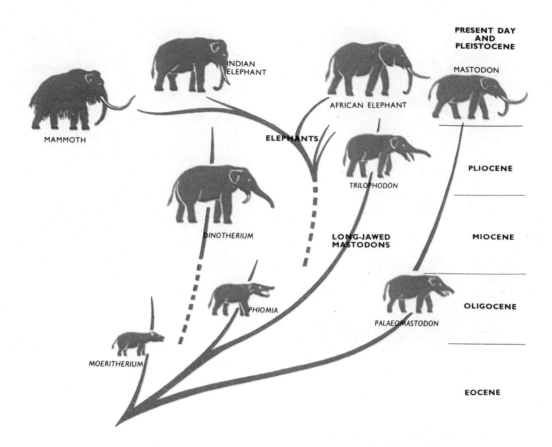

PRESENT DAY
AND
PLEISTOCENE

MASTODON

INDIAN ELEPHANT

ELEPHANTS

AFRICAN ELEPHANT

PLIOCENE

MAMMOTH

TRILOPHODON

DINOTHERIUM

LONG-JAWED MASTODONS

MIOCENE

PHIOMIA

OLIGOCENE

PALAEOMASTODON

MOERITHERIUM

EOCENE

The family tree of elephants. Some of the lines have unknown origins but all must have come from an ancestor like Moeritherium. *The nearest living relatives of the elephants are the small hyraxes and the sea-cows which are grouped with them as* sub-ungulates.

differ in a number of details. Until the beginning of this century, even these were in danger of extinction. Now they are given some protection and numbers are increasing again.

The most obvious thing about elephants is their size – a fully grown African specimen may be more than eleven feet high at the shoulder and may weigh seven tons. The Indian elephant is usually slightly smaller and there are sub-species such as the African forest elephant only about eight feet tall. Elephants are by far the largest of land-living animals. The giraffes top them in height only by virtue of their long slender necks.

To support their great weight the elephants have huge columnar legs which give them a very clumsy appearance. Nevertheless, an elephant can move along at a fair speed – and silently. A cushion of tissue under the foot effectively silences the foot-steps. Although elephants can be trained to get up on their hind legs, they cannot jump at all – their leg structure is not suitable.

The skull is large but relatively light. The bones are full of cavities and channels (*sinuses*) which contain air. Without these cavities, the animal would be unable to lift its head for the tusks alone may weigh three hundred-weight in a large bull elephant. The brain is large although not large in

MAMMOTH

Elephant trunks are derived from the nose and the upper jaw. The tip differs in the various species.

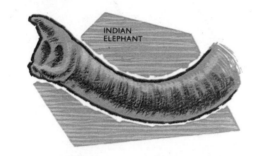
INDIAN ELEPHANT

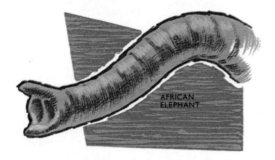
AFRICAN ELEPHANT

Size in Animals

During the evolution of elephants there has been a general tendency to increase in size. This tendency also occurred in many other mammals. Larger size may give an animal more strength or speed. It would thus be an advantage and natural selection would favour the larger ones. This would be especially so in cold climates. The ratio of surface area to volume is lower in large animals and so they lose relatively less heat. However, a large animal needs lots of food and sudden climatic changes may endanger its food supply or otherwise put the animal at a disadvantage. This may be why most of the large elephant types and other early mammals died out.

proportion to the size of the body. The elephant is an intelligent beast whose memory is a well-known feature. The senses of smell and hearing are well developed.

An elephant's trunk acts as another limb – and a very useful one at that. It enables the elephant to get food from the ground and from high in the tree and is also used in drinking – water is sucked into the trunk and then squirted into the mouth. The

The cheek teeth (molars) of a mastodon and an elephant. The mastodon's teeth were small compared with those of the elephant and several were present in the jaws at one time. The tooth of an elephant may be about a foot from front to back.

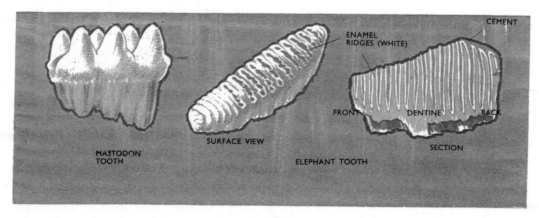
CEMENT

ENAMEL RIDGES (WHITE)

MASTODON TOOTH

SURFACE VIEW

FRONT   DENTINE   BACK

SECTION

ELEPHANT TOOTH

trunk consists of many bands of muscles and it can be shortened, stretched or curved in any direction. It is extremely sensitive to touch – especially at the tip.

Elephants are vegetarians and a full-grown one may eat up to five hundredweight of grass and leaves each day. It is little wonder that they destroy their habitats when large numbers are concentrated in small areas. An elephant's digestion is not very good, however, for the faeces contains a lot of unaltered plant material. This is in spite of the huge grinding surfaces of the cheek teeth.

There is only one fully-functional cheek tooth in each half of each jaw at any one time. This is made up of plates of enamel and dentine which stand up as ridges above the cement to make the grinding surfaces. As each tooth wears down it is replaced by another growing from behind it. The old tooth is gradually resorbed into the body and the last remains fall out. During its life the elephant grows only twenty-four

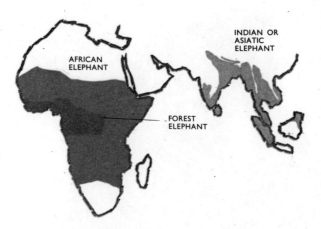

The distribution of living elephants. A subspecies in Africa – the African Forest Elephant – is considerably smaller than the typical form, being only seven or eight feet at the shoulder when fully grown.

cheek teeth – six in each half of each jaw. When the last teeth are worn down the animal will die of starvation for it cannot feed. Most elephants probably die of other causes, however, before this stage is reached. In the wild, fifty years is probably a good age for an elephant.

CHAPTER THIRTY-FOUR

Beavers

MANY animals perform elaborate feats of construction, manipulating their surroundings so that they have somewhere to rear their offspring, store food, hide from enemies and shelter from the elements. But none constructs on the same scale as beavers. These creatures, some three feet long and weighing about forty pounds, are able to build dams up to a hundred yards long and twelve feet high. They fell trees several feet in circumference, construct canals a fifth of a mile or more in length along which they float logs and branches, and build elaborate 'air-conditioned' houses with underwater entrances. They may also dig into the banks of streams forming intricate networks of tunnels many feet long.

However, though these feats are impressive and *suggest* intelligent action, often the dams are not built in the most suitable places and beavers have been observed to spend many hours unnecessarily reinforcing completed dams and building others nearby for no apparent reason. There

(left) An adult beaver. In felling a tree the beaver props itself up on its tail, with its hind legs spread apart and the claws of the forefeet grasping the trunk. The upper front teeth dig into the bark and grip the trunk of the tree whilst the lower ones chisel out chunks of wood. (below) A beaver pond showing the dam, lodge cutaway and several beavers at work. (right) A plan of the pond.

seems to be an inner compulsion for beavers to dam running water and to carry out 'repair' work.

Species of beaver

There are two species of true beavers (the Mountain beaver is not related), the European beaver (*Castor fiber*) and the Canadian or North American beaver (*Castor canadensis*). They are so similar that it is doubtful if they are in fact separate species. The North American beaver is widely distributed over northern parts of the United States of America and Canada, but the European beaver is one of Europe's rarest mammals being found in any numbers only in Southern Norway. The habits of the two species are similar but the European beaver, in areas where it is scarce, tends to live in burrows made in river banks and does not perform the elaborate building activities of its North American cousin.

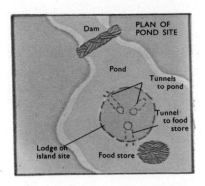

an hour. Its fur is two-layered, an inner fine layer – the beaver skin that is so highly valued by the fur trade – and an outer layer of longer coarse protective hairs that grow out beyond the inner hairs. The 'grain' of the hair is from front to rear so the friction between body and water in swimming is kept to a minimum.

Beavers are best known for their engineering activities. Their tools are four sharp, orange-yellow front teeth, used as chisels, and the fore feet which are equipped with sharp tough claws and used for burrowing. The toes of the fore feet are not webbed and can be used in a similar manner to our fingers to grasp logs and branches. They are their trowels as well, for the beavers spend much of their time stopping up gaps in the dam and cementing branches together with mud.

Building activities

The dam is built across a stream to form a pond for the house or lodge site. The beavers work above the dam, which is constructed of logs, branches, stones and mud, in an area where there are ample supplies of the trees from which they eat the bark. These include poplar, aspen, cotton-wood and willow.

The lodge may be built on the edge of the pond or on a natural small island. Sometimes it is built round a small, bushy tree. It is a domed structure constructed of piled-up branches cemented together with mud. Often it rests on a foundation of boughs and mud which may itself rest on a layer of peat and moss. Only the branches making up the walls are cemented together; the domed roof consists of uncemented branches so that the hollow chamber within is properly ventilated, even in the depth

Characteristics

The beaver's streamlined body is highly suited to fast underwater swimming. A characteristic feature is the broad, flat, scaly tail, often a foot long and dark grey-brown in colour. This versatile structure acts as an oar and a rudder, a prop to lean on, and when it is slapped rapidly on the surface of the water it informs others of approaching danger up to a distance of half a mile. The front limbs are folded backwards under the chest when a beaver is swimming. Only the upper part of the head remains above water. Movements of the hind limbs propel it along. The toes of the hind limbs are webbed. A beaver is able to remain submerged for as long as a quarter of of winter. The floor of the chamber is always a little above the level of the pond and may be stepped so that the sleeping 'quarters' are above the wet openings of the entrance and exit tunnels. They provide access to the underwater store of branches and to the rest of the pond. The tunnels go underground for a short distance opening underwater into the pond.

In felling a tree the beaver props itself up on its tail, with its hind legs spread apart and the claws of the forefeet grasping the trunk. The front teeth gnaw their way through the bark into the wood. Large chunks are torn out until eventually the tree falls over. The beaver does not control the direction in which the tree falls by cutting on a particular side, for beavers are known to have been killed by falling trees. The trunk is cut into shorter lengths – five feet or so, the length depending on the distance that the logs have to be moved – and the logs are dragged into the water and floated downstream to the site of the dam. The logs and branches cut are green and so they sink readily. They are weighted down with stones and mud, being laid parallel to the flow of the stream, though the current may disturb them. The finished dam holds back the water so that it is sufficiently deep for the beaver to enter its lodge and reach its underwater food store in winter when the pond is frozen over. A gap ensures that excess water flows away out of the pool so that its level stays the same. Several dams may be built down-stream of the lodge and one or more may be built up-stream. The beaver uses branches and logs for building the dam and the lodge and also keeps a store near the lodge on the pond floor for its winter food supply. Mud and sticks are packed between the larger branches to plug any holes. The beaver often builds canals to facilitate the transport of logs over long distances.

Social groups

Each pond is inhabited by a small family group of up to twelve individuals. The group often consists of one male and female together with their last two litters. The young mature in their third year and are then expelled from the social group. The arrangement of the group is probably the same in the European beaver. It is thought that each group acts as a whole in defending the pond and its immediate vicinity against enemies.

The mature males and females pair between January and early March and the young are born from May onwards, the numbers varying from one to eight (average three to four).

Beavers eat mainly the bark of trees (especially those mentioned previously), but in summer their diet is supplemented by young shoots, roots and also leaves.

The beaver's pond provides a home for many other creatures – fishes, frogs, waterbirds and small mammals such as musk-rats. Man regards it as an efficient firebreak and a ready supply of water for fighting forest fires. The ponds also help to conserve water that would otherwise flow away from the vicinity and they help regulate the flow of flood waters, thus slowing down erosion.

Index